AI LITERACY FUNDAMENTALS

HELPING YOU JOIN THE

AI CONVERSATION

BEN JONES
CO-FOUNDER & CEO
DATA LITERACY

Illustrated by Alli Torban

First edition published 2024
by Data Literacy Press
500 108th Ave NE, Suite 1100, Bellevue, WA 98004
https://dataliteracy.com

Library of Congress Control Number: 2024934908

Description: First edition. | Bellevue: Data Literacy Press, 2024

ISBN: 978-1-960907-07-3 (paperback)
ISBN: 978-1-960907-08-0 (eBook)

Cover design and interior graphics designed by Alli Torban

Printed in the United States of America.

For Aaron,
whose face the face recognition model
keeps thinking is mine

More by Ben Jones

THE DATA LITERACY SERIES

Data Literacy Fundamentals

Learning to See Data

Read, Write, Think Data

OTHER BOOKS

Leading in the Age of Data

ChatGPT Basics

The Introspective Entrepreneur

Avoiding Data Pitfalls

Communicating Data with Tableau

This book is a companion to the AI Literacy Fundamentals online course which can be found at https://dataliteracy.com/ai-literacy-fundamentals/

Contents

Preface

When I was a boy growing up in California, I loved to go to Zuma Beach and ride the waves in the ocean on my Morey Bodyboard, using my blunt-cut swim fins to zip around and catch the waves, staying nice and low on the face of the wave. Every now and then, a much larger wave would show up on the horizon. I could see the swell gathering and rising ominously as it approached the shore.

At first, my instinct was to swim away from the wave as fast as I could in order to avoid the "crunch zone," the spot where the wave would break and crash. Eventually, I learned (the hard way) that a much better strategy in such a situation is to swim *toward* the wave, racing to meet its face before it breaks.

Artificial intelligence, or AI, is like a massive set of waves that is upon us. By picking up this book, you're making the decision to swim toward the waves. I commend you for that decision. Maybe you made it naturally and without a second thought, filled with curiosity and wonder. Or maybe this decision was as difficult for you as it was for me to bring myself to turn my board around to face the coming wave. Change can be scary.

But AI is not going away. It is going to just keep coming, wave after wave. Some of us will be caught in the crunch zone. Some of us who are more ambitious, privileged, and/or fortunate will ride the wave of AI in glorious fashion. And others of us will be content to hang in there, applying grit and resolve to keep our heads above the water. And that would be a fine outcome.

Whether we thrive or merely survive, we'll need to educate ourselves and keep our eyes and ears open as the AI ocean continues to fluctuate around us. This quote by Mark Cuban captures the stark reality very well:

"Artificial Intelligence, deep learning, machine learning – whatever you're doing if you don't understand it – learn it. Because otherwise you're going to be a dinosaur within three years."

My hope is that, whatever you're doing, this book helps you to begin to learn about AI. I've written it for beginners who are just getting started in their understanding. I believe it will also be beneficial for those who already have a basic level of familiarity with AI, but who seek additional clarity and perspective. In either case, this book will serve as one important part of your learning process. As the waves of technology keep coming, that learning process will only continue.

My hope is that we'll all hang in there, and eventually ride the waves together!

Ben Jones
Palm Springs, California
February 22, 2024

Introduction

We are living in a fascinating period of time. For adults, in the first few decades of the 21st century, technology has advanced a great deal since we were born. The personal computer revolution of the 1970s and 1980s gave way to the rapid spread of the internet in the 1990s and early 2000s. The simultaneous developments in mobile devices, computing power, and digital storage since the turn of the century have led to the proliferation of data: from text in websites, digitized books, and message boards, to photographs uploaded to social media platforms, to streaming video capturing our moments as they unfold.

All of this data has fundamentally transformed our world. The way we work, the way we transact, the way we interact with each other, and the way we live our lives in the modern world are very different from the ways of our parents and our grandparents. It isn't too surprising, then, that our forebears didn't really know how to prepare us for today's world. And so we are faced with the challenge of grasping concepts and acquiring skills that we weren't taught during our years of formal education. Failing to do so means falling behind.

Increasing Pace and Stakes

As much as technology has evolved since we were young, it is evolving at an even faster rate right now. We are in the early phases of an artificial intelligence (AI) revolution whose launch was fueled in part by the dramatic increases in available data and computing power. Combine these environmental factors with advances in machine learning, the branch of AI that focuses on computers that can learn from data, and AI can now do tasks for us that require a significant level of intelligence.

As powerful as AI has become, it is, of course, far from perfect. AI models and programs make many mistakes, they aren't always fair, and they are causing a lot of disruption to entire industries and societies. Many people are not yet familiar with these technologies, and many do not feel comfortable with them. They read the posts and comments on social media about AI, they see news programs about it, and they hear people talking about it at work, but they don't feel confident enough to join those conversations. They're worried about falling even further behind.

Who Is This Book For?

This book is for anyone who wants to join the AI conversation happening in their workplace, in their social media feeds, or in their community. This book is for anyone who wants to learn about AI so they can start harnessing its power while avoiding its pitfalls. This book is the first step in a journey of continuous learning about AI, and it's a critical step to take, whether you're apprehensive or enthusiastic.

It's not just critical for you and your own career that you join the AI conversation. It's critical for all of us that as many of us as possible become educated about AI so that we can share our ideas, our concerns, and our perspectives. The future of AI is in our hands, and the best path forward is the one that's collectively paved by people of different backgrounds, disciplines, and persuasions. An AI that works for all of us must be built by all of us.

What's In This Book?

Part 1: Introduction to AI

The book is organized into three parts, each containing two chapters. In the first part, **Introduction to AI**, we'll start by asking a simple but surprisingly tricky question, "What is AI?" Definitions are important, but as you'll see, the definition of AI has shifted over the years, and it's challenging to pin down even today. On top of that, the various types and levels of AI can be confusing, so we'll compare and contrast different terms and acronyms so you can keep them all straight. We'll gain some additional clarity at the end of this first chapter by considering a short list of familiar, everyday applications that use AI.

In the second chapter, we'll go on a brief and abbreviated tour through the history of AI. We'll start with its enthusiastic beginnings in the middle of the 20th century, navigate our way through multiple droughts or "AI winters" of reduced funding and interest, and end up at the present time, the AI revolution that has been gathering steam in the first few decades of the 21st century. You learn about many of the pioneers of AI, pause to consider some of its major milestones, and gain valuable insight into how the field has evolved.

Part 2: AI Technologies

In the second part of the book, titled **AI Technologies**, we'll look more closely at the branch of AI that has been responsible for virtually all of the major leaps in the recent evolution of AI: **machine learning**. In the third chapter, on machine learning basics, you'll learn about the concept of using data to train computers to perform intelligent tasks instead of giving them explicit, step-by-step instructions on how to do those tasks. You'll also learn about the most common approaches to training computers in this way.

Then, in the fourth chapter, you'll receive a primer on **deep learning**, a special branch of machine learning involving deep neural networks. These powerful AI models consist of multiple layers of interconnected units, or nodes, originally inspired by the function of the biological neurons in our brains. They take digital inputs, multiply them by weights, or parameters, and pass along the resulting signal to the units in the next layer of the network. By adjusting their weights during training, we can make deep neural networks perform one of many tasks once considered to be major challenges for computers, such as recognizing faces and translating text from one language to another.

Part 3: Important Considerations in AI

The third part of the book, **Important Considerations in AI**, represents a shift from the technical aspects of AI to the personal and the societal aspects. In the fifth chapter, we'll consider the many wonderful benefits of AI, and also the serious concerns that it raises, from fears of job displacement to the unfair impacts of algorithmic bias. AI is a powerful set of technologies that can help us in many ways, but that can also do a great deal of harm, depending on how we use them. We'll consider what we can do to realize the promises of AI while dealing with the problems that accompany them.

If the fifth chapter is about cutting through the hype and fear, then the sixth and final chapter is about separating fact from fiction. There are many myths and misconceptions about AI swirling around conversations online and in the real world. In order to be able to participate in these conversations, we need to understand the extreme perspectives out there so that we can articulate reasonable, balanced truths.

Data Literacy and AI Literacy

What is AI literacy? **AI literacy** is the ability to recognize, grasp, use, and critically assess artificial intelligence technologies and their impacts. How does it compare with data literacy? Well, **data literacy** has been defined as the ability to read, understand, create, and communicate data as information. You can think of AI literacy and data literacy as siblings.

Here's the catch, though: true AI literacy requires data literacy. The reason for this is that AI is largely based on and influenced by data. How could someone understand an AI model without having at least a basic understanding of the data that was used to train it? For that reason, I strongly recommend that readers of this book also devote some time to build a firm foundation in data literacy.

An investment in both data and AI literacy will pay great dividends. These two competencies go hand in hand. We need to speak the language of data and AI no matter what our line of work. To be able to read and write in any foreign language, we first need to learn the terms and phrases, along with their meanings. It also helps to observe and listen carefully to others using the language. Eventually, to continue growing in fluency, we need to actively participate by communicating in that language.

My sincere hope is that *AI Literacy Fundamentals* helps you lay a firm foundation in the language of AI so that you can continue to build on that foundation in the years to come. I wish you all the best! If you feel that you are currently at a disadvantage with respect to AI, then just remember the wise words of Lieutenant Commander Data on *Star Trek: The Next Generation*:

The real secret is turning disadvantage into advantage.

PART 1

Introduction to AI

CHAPTER 1

What Is AI?

"It is the science and engineering of making intelligent machines..."
– John McCarthy, the "father" of AI

What is artificial intelligence, or AI? The question might bring to mind images of robot characters in science fiction movies and books, some of them lovable and others menacing. Perhaps a news article surfaces in your memory about a major technological breakthrough, or a writer's union strike, or an initiative or resolution that was passed by Congress. Or maybe you can't help but think of all the marketing hype and social media buzz that seems to focus on the term these days. Talk of artificial intelligence seems to pop up everywhere, but what exactly is it?

Defining AI

It turns out that it's surprisingly difficult to answer this question, at least to everyone's satisfaction. The person who coined the term in 1955, Stanford professor John

McCarthy, defined it as "the science and engineering of making intelligent machines, especially intelligent computer programs." This definition is helpful because it clears up what McCarthy meant by "artificial" – in a word, computers. Notice, however, that he used the word "intelligent" twice in the definition itself. And therein lies the challenge: we don't always mean the same thing when we call something intelligent.

For example, when a child aces a difficult math exam, we say she's quite intelligent. When a dog alerts us to its owner's high blood sugar levels, we say it's remarkably intelligent. Some even say that trees can exhibit an uncanny form of intelligence, such as the way an acacia tree releases ethylene gas when a giraffe starts chewing on its leaves, causing neighboring trees to pump tannins into their own leaves to ward off the threat. These actions, and many more, might all fall into the category of intelligent actions, but they're quite different from each other, aren't they?

If we struggle to succinctly define the intelligence of biological lifeforms, then it makes sense that we'd struggle to do so for agents that aren't biological, such as digital computers. Which actions can a computer take that we would call "intelligent?" Does it need to answer specific questions correctly or hold a conversation with us for a certain amount of time? Does it need to be able to drive a car across town without crashing, or recognize your face in a photograph, or beat a grandmaster at chess? Does it need to be able to create poignant music or art or poetry, or tell a funny, original joke? Does it need to be able to perform some or all of these actions, not just one of them?

You'll probably get a variety of answers if you were to ask your friends or coworkers, "What is artificial intelligence?" For humans, animals, and computers alike, there are different types and levels of intelligence. It's very difficult to wrap our arms around all of it. What seems like very intelligent behavior to one person might be totally basic or trite to another. And so the difficulty in precisely defining artificial intelligence is one aspect about it that we'll all need to embrace. Even a committee of dozens of industry experts acknowledged as recently as 2016 "the lack of a precise, universally accepted definition of AI."[1]

In spite of that, let's look at a few definitions of artificial intelligence to see if we can extract some value from them. We'll start with the definition we find in the dictionary itself. The *Oxford English Dictionary* provides the following definition for "artificial intelligence:"

> *"The capacity of computers or other machines to exhibit or simulate intelligent behaviour; the field of study concerned with this."*[2]

This definition isn't very different from McCarthy's, and it begs the exact same question, namely, what is intelligent

1. "The One Hundred Year Study of Artificial Intelligence (AI100)." Stanford University, 2021, ai100.stanford.edu.
2. *Oxford English Dictionary*, s.v. "artificial intelligence, n.," July 2023, https://doi.org/10.1093/OED/3194963277.

behavior? It does, however, add one helpful distinction: the term can also refer to the *field of study* concerned with such behavior. Artificial intelligence isn't just the name we use to describe a certain type of computer system; it's also the name we use to describe the field that studies and creates such systems. And so there are AI departments at universities, AI teams within companies, and AI experts on government panels.

Speaking of governments, let's consider another definition provided by one. Governments around the world are, understandably, very interested in artificial intelligence. The U.S. federal government is certainly no exception. Referring to artificial intelligence and quantum computing, U.S. Secretary of State Antony J. Blinken stated that "a global technology revolution is now underway."[3] When the U.S. Congress passed the National Artificial Intelligence Initiative Act of 2020, they provided this definition:[4]

> *"The term 'artificial intelligence' means a machine-based system that can, for a given set of human-defined objectives, make predictions, recommendations, or decisions influencing real or virtual environments. Artificial intelligence systems use machine and human-based inputs to –*
>
> *(A) perceive real and virtual environments;*

3. U.S. Department of State. "Secretary Blinken's remarks at the NSCAI Global Emerging Technology Summit, in Washington, D.C." YouTube, uploaded July 13, 2021, www.youtube.com/watch?v=EwHOtVvJcU0
4. Title 15, Sec. 9401. U.S. Code. 2024, https://uscode.house.gov/view.xhtml?req=(title:15%20section:9401%20edition:prelim.

> *(B) abstract such perceptions into models through analysis in an automated manner; and*
>
> *(C) use model inference to formulate options for information or action."*

This definition adds quite a lot, doesn't it? Notice that it doesn't use the term "intelligent" anywhere in its definition. Instead, it lists specific types of actions, such as perception of environments, abstraction into models, and formulation of options. These verbs give us a lot more to draw from, especially the notion of creating models, which we'll revisit. But it also introduces a host of challenging questions.

What, for example, does it mean to *perceive* something? Does the machine-based system just need to register a change in the environment via some sensory input like a camera or a microphone, or does it actually need to have conscious awareness of such a change? This question opens a can of worms related to the nature of consciousness, a fascinating topic in the study of philosophy of mind that we won't explore together in this book. The true nature of our own consciousness, after all, remains an open question.

Why don't we give an AI a chance to define itself? I turned to one of the most advanced AI chatbots in the world today, OpenAI's ChatGPT, and was given the following definition:

> *"Artificial Intelligence (AI) refers to the simulation of human intelligence in machines that are designed to*

> *think, learn, and make decisions or actions that would typically require human intelligence. This includes tasks like problem-solving, recognizing patterns, understanding natural language, and perception. AI systems can be programmed to perform these tasks through various approaches, including rules-based methods, machine learning, and deep learning. The ultimate goal of AI is to create systems that can perform complex tasks autonomously and adaptively, often improving their performance over time as they gain more experience or data."*[5]

Wow, that's a lot! Just what is the AI that generated this definition for us? The version of ChatGPT I interacted with used OpenAI's GPT-4, which is an instance of a **large language model** (**LLM**), a form of AI we'll discuss in more detail later in this book. GPT stands for "Generative Pre-trained Transformer." It has been trained on a massive corpus of text from the internet and books to predict the next word in a sentence, resulting in remarkable conversational abilities, at least by today's standards. Whether people a year or a decade from now will consider GPT-4's capabilities to be remarkable is another matter. Time will tell.

In very rough terms, then, ChatGPT can be thought of as summarizing popular text written about a topic. It's important to note, however, that its output is influenced

5. OpenAI. "ChatGPT Response on the Definition of AI." OpenAI's ChatGPT, GPT-4, 3 December 2023, private correspondence.

by the human feedback it has received during its development. Its output is also subject to constraints, called "safeguards," that are designed to prevent it from slipping into various forms of undesirable outputs, such as hateful content or content that could expose **personally identifiable information** (**PII**), such as Social Security numbers, passport numbers, personal addresses, or telephone numbers.

So, going back to the definition it provided, how well did it do defining itself? I'd say it did fairly well, even if it also subjected itself to the same thorny philosophical debates, such as what it means to "think," "understand," and "perceive." It introduced important terms we'll consider later in this book, such as machine learning and deep learning, although it didn't attempt to explain what these terms mean.

Its definition is certainly wordier than the other definitions we've just considered. When I gave ChatGPT a follow-up prompt asking for a more concise definition, here's how it responded:

> *"Artificial Intelligence (AI) is the development of computer systems that can perform tasks typically requiring human intelligence, such as visual perception, speech recognition, decision-making, and language translation."*[6]

6. Ibid.

Once again, these two definitions – both the original, longer one and the revised, shorter one – use the word "intelligence" to define a form of intelligence. Notice, in particular, these AI-generated definitions relate artificial intelligence to human intelligence. According to GPT-4, the nature of the relationship is that artificial intelligence is designed to *simulate* human intelligence in various ways, and to perform tasks typically requiring human intelligence.

As these technologies continue to evolve, and as AI applications and systems arise that can perform more and more tasks beyond the reach of human intelligence, it will be interesting to see whether or not the various definitions of artificial intelligence continue mentioning human intelligence. What happens, for example, when an AI's capabilities surpass our own? In many ways, they already have. For example, some programs can already process, categorize, and summarize text much faster than we can. Others can beat us at some of our most cherished games. Still others can find patterns that we struggle to find in massive repositories of data. If they can do these tasks faster and better than we can, are they still simulating our intelligence, or are they taking on a form of intelligence all their own?

The AI Effect

There's an important point to mention relative to the evolution of artificial intelligence that can help us appreciate the ongoing challenge of defining it. There's a phenomenon called the **AI effect**, sometimes called the **AI paradox.** In a nutshell, it says that once a problem thought to require intelligence is solved by a computer, we tend to stop thinking of the problem as requiring "true" intelligence, and, by natural extension, we no longer think of the solution itself as being AI. It's a classic case of moving the goalposts.

A common example involves the ancient game of chess, once thought to be the quintessential test of intelligence. Surely if a computer could defeat the world's greatest chess player, everyone would agree that it must be highly intelligent. Well, that's just what IBM's Deep Blue did in 1997, defeating world champion Garry Kasparov 3½–2½ in a rematch in New York City.[7]

In the immediate aftermath, Deep Blue's victory was widely hailed as a major milestone in artificial intelligence. Soon afterward, however, critics and analysts downplayed Deep Blue's approach to be nothing more than powerful computation, along with an extensive database of moves to look up. They even began to downplay chess itself, dismissing it as an activity that can be approached with brute-force computation, as opposed to with actual intelligence. The bar, evidently, had been raised.

For example, neuroscientist Jeff Hawkins, co-founder of Palm Computing, wrote the following in his 2005 book, *On Intelligence: How a New Understanding of the Brain Will Lead to the Creation of Truly Intelligent Machines*:

7. Weber, Bruce. "Swift and Slashing, Computer Topples Kasparov." ***New York Times,*** May 12, 1997, https://www.nytimes.com/1997/05/12/nyregion/swift-and-slashing-computer-topples-kasparov.html.

"Deep Blue didn't win by being smarter than a human; it won by being millions of times faster than a human....It played chess yet didn't understand chess, in the same way a calculator performs arithmetic but doesn't understand mathematics."[8]

Even Kasparov himself shared a similar perspective in his book *Deep Thinking: Where Machine Intelligence Ends and Human Creativity Begins*:

"Deep Blue was intelligent the way your programmable alarm clock is intelligent. Not that losing to a $10 million alarm clock made me feel any better."[9]

Similar shifts have occurred following breakthroughs in **speech recognition**, which everyone's smartphone or virtual assistant (e.g. Amazon's Alexa) is now capable of performing, as well as **optical character recognition (OCR)**, which we all benefit from anytime we take a photograph of a check in order to deposit it into our bank account. These capabilities and many others were once thought to be considerable challenges for computers, but many people now feel that such everyday applications can't possibly be examples of artificial intelligence.

8. Hawkins, Jeff, and Sandra Blakeslee. *On Intelligence: How a New Understanding of the Brain Will Lead to the Creation of Truly Intelligent Machines.* Times Books, 2004.
9. Kasparov, Garry, and Mig Greengard. *Deep Thinking: Where Machine Intelligence Ends and Human Creativity Begins.* PublicAffairs, 2018.

One can only wonder how future generations will come to think of breakthroughs in artificial intelligence that are only a gleam in our eye today. So it goes. We have a way of quickly adjusting our mindset to take for granted what was previously unimaginable, don't we? Today's mind-blowing new feature becomes tomorrow's basic functionality. As John McCarthy himself once famously said, "As soon as it works, no one calls it AI anymore." As the AI effect illustrates, the definition of AI has been a moving target.

Strong AI versus Weak AI

Most AI experts feel, though, that even today's most mind-blowing new AI features do not amount to what is called **strong AI**. Also called **general AI** or **artificial general intelligence** (**AGI**), strong AI is a hypothetical type of AI that, if created, could learn to perform any action that humans are able to perform. Its intelligence, then, would be very broad, and it would be capable of image detection, language processing, reasoning, problem-solving, decision-making across multiple, diverse domains, and more.

Strong AI is hypothetical because it has never been created. Some AI experts believe that it is a long way off, and not all of them believe it's even possible to develop such a system. Others, however, are more enthusiastic about the possibilities. Take OpenAI, for example. OpenAI is an AI research organization founded in 2015 and headquartered in San Francisco. The stated mission of OpenAI is "to ensure that artificial general intelligence – AI systems that are generally smarter than humans – benefits all of humanity."[10] Notice their decision to define AGI as *smarter than* humans rather than merely *as smart as* humans.

Strong AI stands in contrast to **weak AI**, also called **narrow AI**, or **artificial narrow intelligence (ANI)**. Weak AI refers to any artificial intelligence that has been designed and created to solve a single problem or a very limited set of problems. Examples of weak AI are all around us, carrying out specific tasks that normally require a human to carry out, while having no ability whatsoever to carry out any other kind of task.

Artificial Narrow Intelligence (ANI)

- Sometimes called Weak AI
- Narrow AI
- Performs only specialized tasks
- Widespread in usage

Artificial General Intelligence (AGI)

- Sometimes called Strong AI
- Human-level AI
- Can be applied broadly
- Hypothetical (hasn't been created yet)

Figure 1.1. Differences between strong AI and weak AI

10. Altman, Sam. "Planning for AGI and Beyond." OpenAI Blog, OpenAI, February 24, 2023, https://openai.com/blog/planning-for-agi-and-beyond.

IBM's Deep Blue, for example, was great at chess but it couldn't play Monopoly at all, let alone tell you if a photo showed a cat or a dog. The recommendation system on an ecommerce website may be very sophisticated and make excellent suggestions to a wide range of potential customers, but in today's world, it cannot yet drive your car.

Don't be fooled by the term, though, because such systems sometimes have anything but a weak impact on our world. Weak AI is everywhere, and these technologies have dramatically changed many aspects of work, society, and even life itself.

We're starting to see examples of relatively sophisticated forms of weak AI that have been given "multimodal" capabilities, such as when OpenAI added voice and image recognition to its popular AI chatbot, ChatGPT.[11] The rate and the nature of these advances is very difficult to predict, making it virtually impossible to guess how far away we are from something resembling AGI. What is helpful, though, is to understand the distinction between these two forms of AI, so that we can evaluate the technology as it evolves.

General Purpose AI (GPAI)

To muddy the waters somewhat, a relatively new term (and associated four-letter acronym!) entered the AI lexicon in 2021, making its formal debut in an amendment to the

11. OpenAI, "ChatGPT Can Now See, Hear, and Speak." OpenAI Blog, September 25, 2023, https://openai.com/blog/chatgpt-can-now-see-hear-and-speak.

European Union's AI Act, which passed in December 2023. EU Legislators proposed the term **general purpose AI**, or **GPAI**. What did they mean by this term? According to the wording of the 2021 amendment,

> *"(44b) 'general purpose AI model' means an AI model, including when trained with a large amount of data using self-supervision at scale, that displays significant generality and is capable to competently perform a wide range of distinct tasks regardless of the way the model is placed on the market and that can be integrated into a variety of downstream systems or applications."*[12]

Now, there are some "fuzzy" words and phrases in this definition, to be sure, such as "*large amount of data*," (how large?), *"significant generality"* (how significant and how general?), and "*wide range of distinct tasks*" (how wide and how distinct?). Considering the acceleration of progress in AI technologies, these terms might mean something very different in the near future. After all, we scoff at what passed for "big data" just a few years ago.

What we know for sure is that the intent of this relatively new term is to regulate powerful new AI technologies such OpenAI's GPT-4 and Google's Gemini, which were unleashed on the world starting in late 2022. Most AI experts still feel that these large language models (LLMs) fall into the category of ANI, or Weak AI as opposed to AGI, or Strong

12. "EU AI Act, Article 3 Definitions." https://www.euaiact.com/article/3, Last Accessed February 28, 2024.

AI. There are some researchers, however, including a group at Microsoft who do feel that ChatGPT shows the early "sparks" of AGI, and can "reasonably be viewed as an early (yet still incomplete) version of an artificial general intelligence (AGI) system."[13]

I, for one, agree with the majority of AI experts that these powerful LLMs do not currently amount to AGI, nor do they come close, but there's no doubt that they're far more capable than the highly specialized (and therefore far more limited) ANI models of the recent past. They do a lot more than simply classify the sentiment of a social media post as being either positive or negative, or unlock your iPhone screen based on the face picked up by your smartphone's camera. Their multimodal capabilities as well as their conversational capabilities would seem to put them into a different category than single-purpose AI applications. Figure 1.2 shows the relationship between GPAI, ANI, and AGI, at least as I see it.

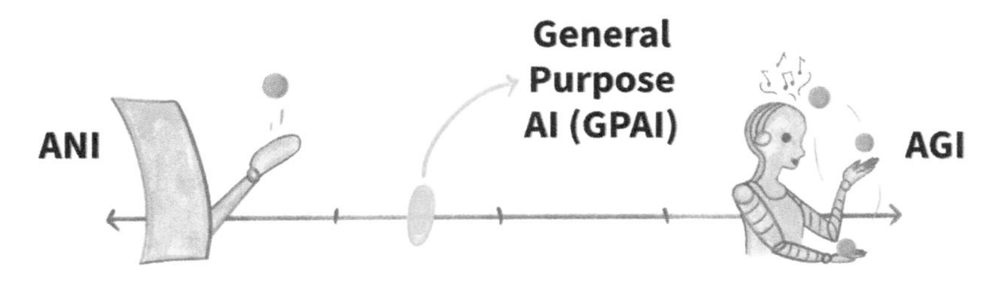

Figure 1.2. How general purpose AI (GPAI) relates to ANI and AGI

13. Bubeck, Sébastien et al. "Sparks of Artificial General Intelligence: Early experiments with GPT-4." ArXiv abs/2303.12712 (2023): n. pag.

Did we need a brand new term and acronym for them? Perhaps. It's unfortunate that this new category also includes the word "general," as it seems likely that many people will confuse general purpose AI with artificial general intelligence. I believe that what we can take from this development is that the gap between AGI and ANI is closing. Regardless of whether the new classification was needed, this new batch of technologies does represent a major leap in the evolution of AI.

Examples in Everyday Life

In order to give you a better understanding of what AI is, let's consider a number of real-world examples that most of us can relate to. Talking about AI as a concept or a theory or a field is one thing, but the fact is that AI has already been employed in numerous aspects of life. Not everyone is aware that these applications involve AI, though.

Streaming Movie Recommendations

You likely subscribe to one or more of the many movie streaming platforms such as Netflix[14] or Hulu. The last time you logged on to watch your favorite show, did you notice a section called "Recommended for you," or "Based on your viewing history," or something like that? How does the platform know what to suggest to you in that section, and

14. "How Netflix's Recommendations System Works." Netflix Help Center, https://help.netflix.com/en/node/100639. Accessed January 2, 2024.

why is it different from what it suggests to someone else in that same section of their account?

These platforms use a form of artificial intelligence called a **recommendation system** (or a **recommender**) to turn search and viewing history, ratings data, and potentially other demographic variables into a prediction about which shows you'll most likely watch and enjoy. But not everyone is aware that they're interacting with AI when using suggestion systems like this. In a February 2023 study, more than a third of Americans surveyed by researchers at Pew Research Center failed to identify such suggestion systems as AI-powered applications that use AI.[15]

Virtual Assistants

Most of us now interact with a variety of virtual assistants such as Amazon's Alexa or Apple's Siri to perform a variety of everyday tasks such as finding out the weather, setting a timer in the kitchen, adding a reminder to our calendar to call someone, creating a grocery shopping list, or learning how much traffic we'll encounter on our morning commute to the office.

We can interact with these assistants in a variety of ways, but they're primarily designed to respond to our voice commands. How do these virtual assistants turn the sound waves that we create with our vocal chords into

15. Kennedy, Brian, Alec Tyson, and Emily Saks. "Public Awareness of Artificial Intelligence in Everyday Activities." Pew Research Center. February 15, 2023. https://www.pewresearch.org/science/2023/02/15/public-awareness-of-artificial-intelligence-in-everyday-activities/.

meaningful answers we can hear back? They use a series of AI components, including voice-to-text **speech recognition** as well as **natural language processing (NLP)** algorithms – both **natural language understanding (NLU)** and **natural language generation (NLG)** – to "talk" with us in this way.

Facial Recognition (or Face Recognition)

How do you unlock your smartphone screen? You can probably enter a secret numerical code, but it's becoming more and more common to use facial recognition software to do so. For example, Apple's Face ID feature,[16] while not foolproof, uses the iPhone's front-facing camera along with thousands of tiny, invisible infrared dots it projects onto the user in order to obtain a 3D image of their face. It then uses technologies from a branch of artificial intelligence called **computer vision** to determine if the face is the correct one, based on the geometry the phone stored when the user first set up the feature.

One remarkable aspect of the technology is that the AI systems can identify a face correctly a high percentage of the time even though the angles and lighting are never exactly the same. And the system is even designed to adjust along with small adjustments to a person's face over time, such as when they grow facial hair or put on makeup. Historically, some facial recognition systems have performed worse for people with darker skin than for

16. "About Face ID Advanced Technology." Apple Support, August 22, 2023, https://support.apple.com/en-us/102381. Accessed January 2, 2024.

FACE DETECTION

- Determines if a face is present.
- Locates the face.
- Initial step in photo tagging and surveillance systems.

FACIAL ATTRIBUTE ANALYSIS

- Determines specific attributes of a face, like emotional state.
- Used in user experience research/marketing analysis.

FACE VERIFICATION

- Determines if a face matches a specific, known face.
- Commonly used in identity verification systems.

FACE IDENTIFICATION

- Determines which face a given face matches in a large database of known faces.
- Controversially used in law enforcement surveillance systems.

Figure 1.3. Different forms of facial recognition

people with lighter skin, and for females than for males, a topic we'll consider in more detail Chapter 5.

Facial recognition isn't just one technology. It can be broken down into four major branches of programs. **Face detection** attempts to determine if a person's face is even present in an image or video, and if so, where the face is located. **Facial attribute analysis** is designed to determine traits of the detected face, such as age, gender, and emotional state. The goal of **face verification** is to determine if a given face matches a specific, known face – the type of program used by your smartphone to unlock your screen. Finally, **face identification** is concerned with determining which face a given face matches in a potentially large database of known faces. These types of programs can be used together in a particular AI, and each of them involves error rates that are shrinking, but still not negligible. Furthermore, error rates have been shown to be worse for certain groups of people than for others, a problem we'll discuss in more detail in Chapter 5.

Email Spam Filtering

Checking our email can be a hazardous act these days! Our inboxes are constantly bombarded with annoying advertisements and, even worse, malicious scams designed to compromise our security and privacy. Who among us hasn't fallen prey to such ridiculousness at some point in life? Luckily, most of these unwanted emails get automatically filtered out of our inboxes and placed into a spam folder for periodic deletion. How does the email platform decide whether an email should be placed into the normal inbox or the spam folder?

Your email platform uses a spam filter that employs **artificial neural networks**, often simply called **neural networks**, to "learn" what type of words and phrases are commonly included in known spam emails they're trained on. Neural networks are computational models loosely inspired by the human brain to learn patterns by a process of trial and error, and we'll consider them in more detail later in this book. The neural networks of your spam filter then use this training to make predictions as emails of unknown nature are received. They continuously adjust the parameters as you mark whether or not particular messages are spam, helping them keep up with the continuously shifting tactics of spammers seeking to bypass the filters and land a message in your inbox.

Machine Translation

If you've ever traveled to a country in which the local population speaks a different language than your own, then you might've used an AI application like Google Translate to find out what a street sign means, or to know how to ask someone where to find the nearest restroom. One of the earliest challenges to which artificial intelligence was applied was **machine translation**, the process of automatically translating from one language to another without the intervention of a human translator.

You can encounter another opportunity to take advantage of significant strides made recently in the field of machine translation by visiting a webpage that's full of text in a foreign language. Modern browsers such as Google Chrome provide a link or button at the top of the webpage that lets you choose to have the browser itself automatically translate the contents of the page into a language of your choice. These AI-powered features are far from perfect, and it's not uncommon for them to provide output that an expert translator would disagree with. But it's hard to argue against the usefulness of an instant translation, even one in which some nuance and subtleties of speech are "lost in translation."

These are just a handful of the many instances and types of artificial intelligence we interact with every single day. For now, we've just touched on them in a very superficial way, from the point of view of the user. In later chapters, we'll consider these and other approaches in more detail as we seek to obtain an even deeper understanding of the nature and impact of artificial intelligence in our world.

Generative AI

A relatively new way of interacting with AI exploded in popularity starting on November 30, 2022, with the launch of ChatGPT by OpenAI. Adoption of ChatGPT reached 100 million users in just two months, faster than any other technology in history.[17] ChatGPT is a product that uses a **large language model**, or **LLM**, that OpenAI designed to generate text responses based on prompts entered by users in everyday language. The large language models behind ChatGPT as of the time of writing, OpenAI's GPT-3.5 and GPT-4, have been trained on a massive corpus of text from websites, books, scientific papers, news articles, and more. In the weeks and months following the launch of ChatGPT, other major technology companies like Google and Baidu rushed to launch their own large language models, and open-source models have quickly increased in availability, as well.

Text isn't the only type of content that generative AI can be designed to create. Products like MidJourney, Stable Diffusion, and OpenAI's DALL•E (incorporated into ChatGPT in October 2023) all generate images based on user-entered prompts, and other programs exist to create video output as well. There are many outstanding questions that generative AI raises, such as their propensity to perpetuate social biases as well as their relationship to the intellectual property rights of the individuals and organizations that created the content on which they were trained. These issues have yet to be resolved, and we'll consider them in more detail in Chapter 5.

17. Hu, Krystal. "ChatGPT Sets Record for Fastest-Growing User Base – Analyst Note." Reuters, February 2, 2023, https://www.reuters.com/technology/chatgpt-sets-record-fastest-growing-user-base-analyst-note-2023-02-01/.

Summary

In this first chapter, we started off by thinking broadly about what AI is, considering definitions from different sources that gave us a better understanding of the variety of perspectives. Definitions of AI often include comparisons to human intelligence, and some get much more specific about what that means, listing different types of actions that AI can take, such as creating models from data and automating analysis for decision-making.

We came to the realization that defining AI is not so simple, partly because the word “intelligence” itself can mean different things, and partly because the definition of AI is not fixed. According to the AI effect, what people consider to be artificial intelligence has changed over time, making it next to impossible to pin down one single, static definition.

It is possible, though, to differentiate between strong AI, or artificial general intelligence (AGI), and weak AI, or artificial narrow intelligence (ANI). The former is a hypothetical type of AI that can solve a wide variety of challenges as well as or better than humans. One has never been created, at least not yet. The latter is a type of AI we can find everywhere around us – programs that can perform a specific task that normally requires a human to carry out.

We rounded out this first chapter by briefly considering six examples of weak AI that can be found in everyday life: recommendation systems, virtual assistants, facial recognition, email spam filtering, machine translation, and generative AI. I hope this chapter gave you a high level appreciation for what AI is, and I hope that it also whetted your appetite for more to come.

In the next chapter, we'll go on a brief tour through the history of AI. An appreciation for where the field has been in the past might just give you a better understanding of where we find ourselves today.

CHAPTER 2

A Brief History of AI

"Machines will be capable, within twenty years, of doing any work that a man can do."[18]
– Herbert A. Simon, 1960

In order to really get to know someone, and to understand why they are the way they are, it can help to consider where they've been. A healthy appreciation of the past can inform our awareness of the present, and to some degree our ability to anticipate the future. The same is true not just of people, but of any topic of interest. With that in mind, let's take a tour through the annals of history to get to know AI a little better. I believe we'll find that getting to know AI actually involves getting to know ourselves, and the path that our own species has taken.

Since ancient times, humans have been fascinated by the notion of machines that behave intelligently. In Greek mythology, the story of Talos, dating to around

18. H. A. Simon, *The Ford Distinguished Lectures, Volume 3: The New Science of Management Decision.* (Harper and Brothers, 1960), p. 38.

400 BCE, provides an early example. According to the myth, Talos was a giant humanoid made entirely of brass by Hephaestus, the god of fire and metalworking. Talos was given to King Minos of Crete in order to guard the island against invaders. When Jason and the Argonauts approached the island after obtaining the Golden Fleece, Talos hurled great boulders at his ship, the *Argo*, to keep them at bay. As the legend has it, Talos was defeated when a bronze nail in his ankle was removed, draining him of the ethereal fluid that brought him to life.

Other such examples of humanlike machines can be found in the folklore of different cultures. The third century BCE Taoist text *Lietzi* contains the curious account of Yan Shi the Artificer, a mechanical engineer who presented to King Mu of Zhou his marvelous invention, a life-sized automaton that could walk and posture and sing perfectly in tune.[19] When the robot began winking at the women in attendance, Yan Shi had to quickly pacify King Mu by taking his invention apart, showing him that it actually was made of materials like leather and wood. Luckily for Yan Shi, King Mu's anger at the automaton's flirtatious behavior was stayed by this dismantling display, which, as the story goes, absolutely delighted the king.

19. Lieh-tzu, *Taoist Teachings*, trans. Lionel Giles (London: Murray, 1912), https://archive.org/details/taoistteachings00liehuoft/page/n5/mode/2up

The Turing Test

In spite of these ancient myths and legends, most AI professionals trace the beginning of their field back to the middle of the 20th century, to the pioneering work of founding members, including the English mathematician Alan Turing and the American computer scientist John McCarthy, along with Marvin Minsky, Claude Shannon, Allen Newell, Herbert A. Simon, and others. The male-dominated origin of AI cannot be denied, and social biases like this continue to overshadow both the field and its creations, as we'll consider in later chapters.

Following his time at Bletchley Park in the 1940s helping the team that cracked the code of the Nazis' cipher device known as the Enigma machine, Alan Turing turned his attention to the question "Can machines think?" Believing the question itself to be "too meaningless to deserve distinction," he published a paper titled "Computing Machinery and Intelligence" in the leading philosophical journal *Mind* in 1950, in which he proposed an alternate question in the form of a game called "the imitation game."[20]

A form of Turing's imitation game, which we now call the **Turing test**, involves three players: 1) a human interrogator or judge, 2) a human contestant, and 3) a machine contestant. The judge, who's separated from the

20. A. M. Turing, "Computing Machinery and Intelligence." ***Mind*** 59 (1950): 433–460, http://dx.doi.org/10.1093/mind/LIX.236.433

contestants, is able to ask questions of both of them via a text-only interface, and attempts to distinguish between the two based on their typed responses. The computer is judged to have passed the test if the judge cannot reliably determine that it's the computer, not the human.

Figure 2.1. A cartoon sketch depicting the Turing test

The Turing test has had an enormous influence on the field of AI, but it has also been highly controversial. Critics have pointed out that it only focuses on language capabilities, it has nothing to do with correctness or accuracy, and it overemphasizes the ability of a program to mimic and even deceive humans. Others have pointed out that the judge who gets fooled may simply be naive, or the chatbot's programmers particularly clever.

While claims of passing the Turing test have surfaced over the years following highly publicized competitions, these claims have been widely refuted, and most experts still feel that it has yet to be passed. Some feel that while it's an interesting artifact of the history of AI, the Turing test isn't really relevant to today's advancements. Will an AI definitively pass the Turing test one day? We'll see. For his part, Alan Turing believed that a computer would be able to perform quite well in his game before his century was over:

> **"I believe that in about fifty years' time it will be possible to programme computers...to make them play the imitation game so well that an average interrogator will not have more than 70% chance of making the right identification after five minutes of questioning."**[21]

This specific criterion – more than a 70% chance after five minutes of conversation – has taken on the status of a litmus test, and even a holy grail, in AI. While Turing's prediction about an AI passing his proposed test before the turn of the 20th century didn't come to pass, in many ways his belief in the expansion of the conversational capabilities of machines was right.

Today's most advanced AI chatbots are compared against each other using a wide variety of different tests and benchmarks (e.g. MMLU, "Measuring Massive Multitask Language Understanding"[22]), but the lure of the Turing test still remains. There's no doubt that what modern AI

21. Ibid.
22. Hendrycks, Dan, Collin Burns, Steven Basart, Andy Zou, Mantas Mazeika, Dawn Song, and Jacob Steinhardt. "Measuring Massive Multitask Language Understanding." ICLR 2021. https://doi.org/10.48550/arXiv.2009.03300

chatbots like ChatGPT can do is quite remarkable, even if it's debatable whether they've passed Turing's test, or ever will be able to actually *think*.

The Birth of the Field of AI

The birth of AI as a formal field of study is most often traced back to an event that took place in Hanover, New Hampshire, during the summer of 1956. Now known simply as the **Dartmouth workshop**, the event was organized by John McCarthy, who at the time was an assistant professor of mathematics at Dartmouth College. This event was to change the course of human history.

The year prior, 28-year-old McCarthy approached the Rockefeller Foundation to request funding of $13,500 for the event (equivalent to around $160,000 in 2024), which would cover salaries, travel, and rent expenses for eight people, as well as sundry other expenses. He was able to persuade Marvin Minsky of Harvard, Nathaniel Rochester of IBM, and Claude Shannon of Bell Labs to join him in formally making the request.

The 1955 document they submitted to the Rockefeller Foundation together, titled "A Proposal for the Dartmouth Summer Research Project on Artificial Intelligence," is widely cited as the introduction of the term "artificial intelligence," coined by McCarthy.[23] Here is how the proposal begins:

> *We propose that a 2 month, 10 man study of artificial intelligence be carried out during the summer of 1956 at Dartmouth College in Hanover, New Hampshire. The study is to proceed on the basis of the conjecture that every aspect of learning or any other feature of intelligence can in principle be so precisely described that a machine can be made to simulate it. An attempt will be made to find how to make machines use language, form abstractions and concepts, solve kinds of problems now reserved for humans, and improve themselves. We think that a significant advance can be made in one or more of these problems if a carefully selected group of scientists work on it together for a summer.*

In the end, the request was approved, and around 20 people in all attended the conference, which lasted somewhere between six and eight weeks starting in June and ending in August 1956. What's remarkable about the workshop is that the topics covered – computers, natural language processing, "neuron nets" (now called neural networks), "self-improvement" (now called machine learning), abstraction, and creativity – continue to define the field today.

23. J. McCarthy, M. Minsky, N. Rochester, et al. "A Proposal for the Dartmouth Summer Research Project on Artificial Intelligence." https://raysolomonoff.com/dartmouth/boxa/dart564props.pdf

The Golden Age of AI, 1956–1974

The Dartmouth workshop may not have resolved any of the challenges identified by these founding members who attended, but it did generate a great deal of enthusiasm and optimism for the field of artificial intelligence as a whole. The first two decades after the workshop have been called "The Golden Age of AI." The founders would eventually find out that the problems they were addressing were much more difficult to solve than they initially thought. Ultimately, though, the workshop served as the liftoff point for a mission that held incredible promise, and that would encounter its share of setbacks.

Logic Theorist

At the Dartmouth workshop in 1956, Allen Newell, Herbert A. Simon, and Cliff Shaw presented their fellow attendees with what some now consider to be the very first artificial intelligence program (though others consider the 1952 checkers-playing program written by Arthur Samuel for the IBM 701 mainframe computer to be the first). Their creation, which they called Logic Theorist, or "The Logic Theory Machine," was a breakthrough that no one at the workshop seemed to fully appreciate at that point. It was able to prove a number of mathematical theorems, and even came up with some new, shorter proofs than were previously known.[24] From its very start, then, the field of AI wasn't

24. A. Newell and H. Simon, "The logic theory machine: A complex information processing system," *IRE Transactions on Information Theory* 2 (no. 3, September 1956): 61-79, doi: 10.1109/TIT.1956.1056797

just about workshops and conferences; it was also about innovating and solving.

Symbolic AI and Subsymbolic AI

Following the Dartmouth workshop, the field began in earnest to make some progress. Most of the early efforts, including Logic Theorist, involved a rules-based approach called **symbolic AI**, one of the two main branches of AI. Symbolic AI involves explicit encoding of knowledge using predefined, human-crafted rules. The word "symbolic" comes from the fact that the knowledge contained in these types of programs takes the form of symbols – words or phrases – that humans can typically understand. The rules encoded into the programs, then, contain logic that mimics human reasoning.

Since symbolic AI was the dominant paradigm in the early days of AI, it's sometimes referred to as "classic AI." Later in the book, we'll contrast this early branch of AI with the other main branch, **subsymbolic AI**, which includes today's dominant AI paradigm, deep learning. In contrast to symbolic AI's rules-based approach, subsymbolic AI focuses on learning and finding patterns from large amounts of data. Its heavy emphasis on artificial neural networks, with their myriad connected nodes, has led some to refer to symbolic AI as "connectionist AI" (more to come on that critically important topic soon).

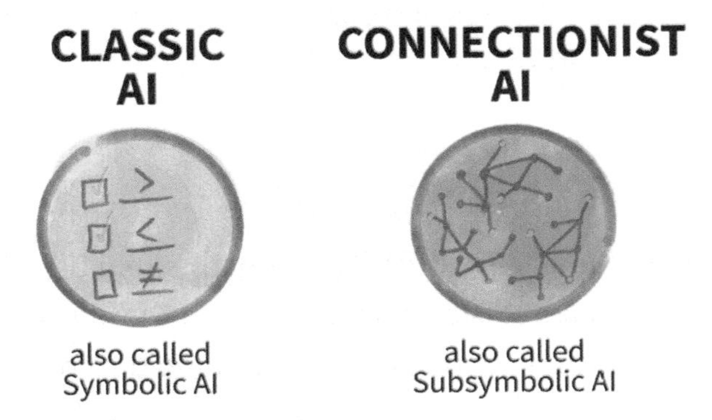

Figure 2.2. An artistic sketch contrasting classic AI with connectionist AI

General Problem Solver

The team that created Logic Theorist went on to develop another rules-based symbolic AI program together. In 1957, Newell, Simon, and Shaw created General Problem Solver, or GPS for short (not to be confused with today's more common usage of GPS to mean Global Positioning System). As the name suggests, GPS was intended to handle a wide variety of problems. Its creators saw it as an attempt to synthesize the problem-solving process itself, and thereby exhibit a form of intelligent behavior.

The design of GPS was informed by observations of college students who were asked to "think aloud" while they solved problems in symbolic logic, such as mathematical proofs or chess moves.

> *GPS-I grew out of an earlier program, the Logic Theorist, which discovers proofs to theorems in the sentential*

> *calculus. GPS-I is an attempt to fit the recorded behavior of college students trying to discover proofs.*[25]

GPS was capable of solving certain types of well-defined logic puzzles, such as the Tower of Hanoi, in which a player must move a stack of disks of decreasing size from one rod to another, moving only one disk at a time, without ever placing a larger disk on top of a smaller one.

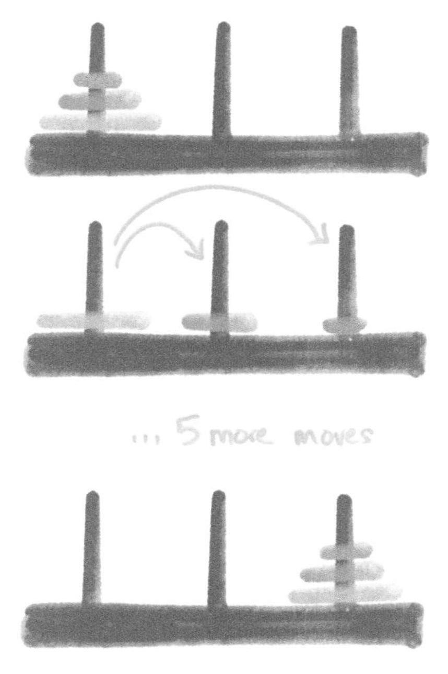

Figure 2.3. A sketch depicting the Tower of Hanoi puzzle

As successful as it was at solving these special types of problems, GPS fell short of being able to solve real-world problems, which tend to be much more complex and

25. A. Newell, J. C. Shaw, and H. A. Simon, "Report on a general problem solving program," *IFIP Congress* 256 (1959): 64.

far messier in their construction than logic puzzles and mathematical proofs. Nevertheless, GPS, like Logic Theorist, represented a major step forward in the history of the field of AI. These early rules-based programs advanced our understanding of how computers could be used to solve problems previously thought to require human intelligence.

ELIZA the "Chatterbot"

If solving textbook problems and puzzles is one aspect of intelligence, then another is being able to engage in a conversation with a human. This is, after all, the very type of behavior that the Turing test is based on. The field of study concerned with this type of behavior is called **Natural Language Processing**, or **NLP**, and it sits at the intersection of AI, computer science, and the field of linguistics. NLP is primarily concerned with giving computers the ability to interact with us using everyday language that we can understand, as opposed to through programming languages, or code.

One of the first attempts to create a computer that could engage in conversation was called ELIZA by its creator, MIT professor Joseph Weizenbaum. Weizenbaum was a German American computer scientist whose Jewish family escaped the Holocaust, settling in Detroit, Michigan, in 1936 when he was 13 years old. He went on to study mathematics at Wayne State University, and then served in the U.S Army Air Corps as a meteorologist during World War II. After returning from service, he completed his undergraduate and graduate degrees in mathematics, and then worked at General Electric before taking a position at the Massachusetts Institute of Technology (MIT) in 1964.

In 1966, while at MIT, Weizenbaum created ELIZA and published the paper "ELIZA – a computer program for the study of natural language communication between man and machine." He named his "chatterbot" – a type of program we now more commonly refer to as an "**AI chatbot**" – after Eliza Doolittle, a fictional character in George Bernard Shaw's 1913 play *Pygmalion*. Doolittle, a character played by Audrey Hepburn in the 1964 musical adaptation *My Fair Lady*, is a poor street vendor ushered into high society and taught to sound and act like a member of London's social elite.

```
  Welcome to
                    EEEEEE  LL      IIII   ZZZZZZ   AAAAA
                    EE      LL       II        ZZ  AA   AA
                    EEEEE   LL       II      ZZZ   AAAAAAA
                    EE      LL       II    ZZ      AA   AA
                    EEEEEE  LLLLLL  IIII ZZZZZZ    AA   AA

  Eliza is a mock Rogerian psychotherapist.
  The original program was described by Joseph Weizenbaum in 1966.
  This implementation by Norbert Landsteiner 2005.

ELIZA: Is something troubling you ?
YOU:   Men are all alike.
ELIZA: What is the connection, do you suppose ?
YOU:   They're always bugging us about something or other.
ELIZA: Can you think of a specific example ?
YOU:   Well, my boyfriend made me come here.
ELIZA: Is it important to you that your boyfriend made you come here ?
YOU:   He says I'm depressed much of the time.
ELIZA: I am sorry to hear that you are depressed.
YOU:   It's true. I am unhappy.
ELIZA: Can you explain what made you unhappy ?
YOU:
```

Figure 2.4. A screenshot of a recreation of ELIZA, by Norbert Landsteiner[26], included with permission[27]

26. N. Landsteiner, "Elizabot." Masswerk, https://www.masswerk.at/elizabot/. Accessed January 12, 2024.

27 File:ELIZA conversation.jpg, Public domain, via Wikimedia Commons, https://commons.wikimedia.org/wiki/File:ELIZA_conversation.png

Like Doolittle, ELIZA was given a set of rules to follow in order to simulate a certain kind of conversation style and, essentially, to fool people. Here's how Weizenbaum described the way his program worked:

> *ELIZA is a program operating within the MAC time-sharing system at MIT which makes certain kinds of natural language conversation between man and computer possible. Input sentences are analyzed on the basis of decomposition rules which are triggered by key words appearing in the text. Responses are generated by reassembly rules associated with selected decomposition rules.*[28]

ELIZA, in other words, couldn't understand human language at all. It was a parlor trick of sorts, an ingenious but relatively simple program consisting of a set of explicit rules to follow to transform a user's typed input into a text response that often gave the user the impression that they were interacting with a real person.

Here's an example of the way ELIZA was designed to interact, as explained by Weizenbaum in his aforementioned paper:

> *YOU: "I am very unhappy these days."*
> *ELIZA: "How long have you been very unhappy these days?"*

28. J. Weizenbaum, "ELIZA – a computer program for the study of natural language communication between man and machine," *Communications of the ACM* 9 (1966): 36–45.

ELIZA's code, triggered in this example by the keywords "I am," followed a rule that produced an output that sounded like a Rogerian (or person-centered) psychotherapist seeking clarifying information, starting with "How long have you been…" As Weizenbaum further explained, a similar response could be produced as follows:

> *YOU: "I am BLAH"*
> *ELIZA: "How long have you been BLAH?"*

ELIZA's code included other similar rules to transform inputs to outputs based on keywords that appeared over the course of the conversation. Was there really a conscious or sentient being inside the program that genuinely wanted to know how long you've been "very unhappy these days," or "BLAH?" Of course not.

But, to his surprise and dismay, Weizenbaum found that many people *felt* like there was someone there behind the responses produced by his clever code. More than that, some people even seemed to form an emotional connection with his program. His own secretary even insisted that he leave the room so that she could continue chatting with ELIZA in private.

This realization disturbed Weizenbaum so much that he went on to speak out in opposition to the direction that the field of AI was taking. He wrote several books criticizing some of his peers and voicing his objections to a world that loses sight of what's special and unique about genuine, human-to-human interactions, especially those involving moral implications, such as in psychotherapy.

While his criticisms sparked much debate within the field of AI, he remained a respected figure in computer science. Weizenbaum died in 2008, so we can only imagine how displeased he would've been with the present-day usage of AI chatbots as agents in online mental health platforms such as Woebot and even as so-called "AI companions" such as Replika that give users the illusion of friendship and romantic connection.

The First AI Winter, 1974–1980

Weizenbaum's magnum opus, *Computer Power and Human Reason,* was a blistering insider critique published in 1976, during the beginning of what has been called the first "**AI winter**." An AI winter is a period of decreasing interest in and funding of research and work in the field. The mid- to late 1970s was the first such lull, but it wasn't the last. In general, the field has been hit by waves of enthusiasm followed by waves of disappointment on the part of the general public that have lasted around a decade each, give or take. Why is this?

There are a variety of reasons why interest in AI has waxed and waned over the years. Indeed, a pronounced "hype cycle" seems to be quite common, with "AI springs" and "AI summers" of increasing interest and activity followed by seemingly inevitable AI winters of retraction and hibernation. In her paper "Why AI is harder than we think," Melanie Mitchell of the Santa Fe Institute describes this pattern as follows:

> *Since its beginning in the 1950s, the field of artificial intelligence has cycled several times between periods of optimistic predictions and massive investment ("AI spring") and periods of disappointment, loss of confidence, and reduced funding ("AI winter").*[29]

The first AI winter that started in the mid-1970s is often explained as a classic case of overpromising and underdelivering. In a nutshell, what happened was this. During the early years of AI, experts in the field made a series of bold predictions and promises about the impending breakthroughs in general capabilities such as natural language and computer vision that didn't quite come to pass. For example, consider the epigraph of this chapter one more time, a painfully overexuberant forecast made by AI pioneer Herbert A. Simon in 1960:

"Machines will be capable, within twenty years, of doing any work that a man can do."

Based on this statement and others like it, it's no wonder that interest in AI surged and then faded. For another example, take the Summer Vision Project of 1966. This

29. Melanie Mitchell. 2021. "Why AI is harder than we think," *Proceedings of the Genetic and Evolutionary Computation Conference* (GECCO '21), Association for Computing Machinery, New York, 3. https://doi.org/10.1145/3449639.3465421

was an initiative organized by Seymour Papert of MIT that aimed to employ a group of about ten undergraduates to construct "a system complex enough to be a real landmark in the development of 'pattern recognition.'"[30] Significant advancements in computer vision, as it turns out, have required much more time and effort than one summer and ten undergraduates.

These promises initially led to high levels of funding and media attention. When they proved to be much more difficult to fulfill than expected, or when what was actually delivered didn't quite live up to its billing, disillusionment predictably set in, attention turned elsewhere, and the funding eventually dried up. As the pattern goes, however, this subsequent period of starvation only set the stage for the next feeding frenzy.

A quick glance at the line chart of the Google Books Ngram Viewer for "artificial intelligence" shows how the frequency of appearance of the term in a corpus of books changed between 1950 and 2019. It's hard to miss both the larger and the smaller surges in usage of the term.

30. Seymour Papert, "The Summer Vision Project," Massachusetts Institute of Technology, Project MAC, 1966.

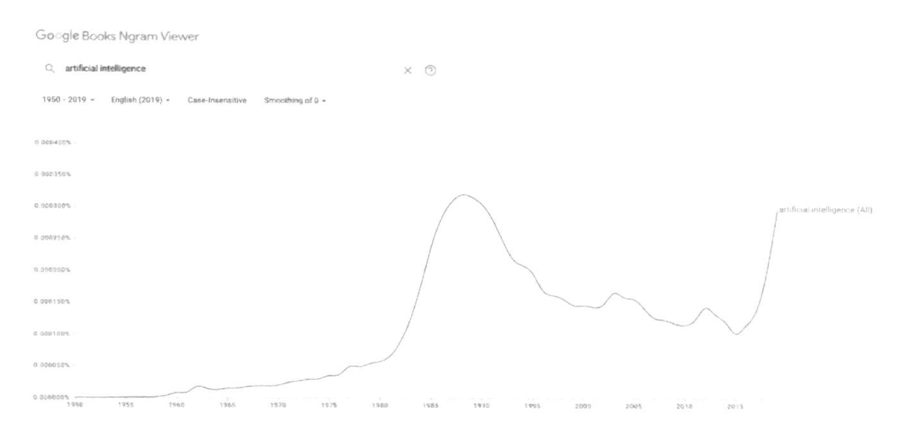

Figure 2.5. Google Ngram search for "artificial intelligence"[31]

The Rise and Fall of Expert Systems, 1980s–Early 1990s

One characteristic of the line chart in Figure 2.5 that's impossible to miss is the dramatic rise of the line in the early 1980s, with its peak around 1987, and subsequent decline in the early 1990s. This bell-like shape of the curve illustrates the AI summer and AI winter pattern quite well, to the degree that we can consider the relative frequency of appearance of a term in books to be a good proxy for overall relevance and popularity of that term.

So what drove this particular rising and falling tide of AI? A look at a second version of the Google Books Ngram Viewer line chart gives a clue about the answer. In Figure 2.6, the line for the term "artificial intelligence" is shown along with

31. Google Books Ngram Viewer, http://books.google.com/ngrams

a second line, which gives the trend for the appearance of the term "expert systems." It's clear from these two lines that their respective surges in the 1980s almost perfectly coincide.

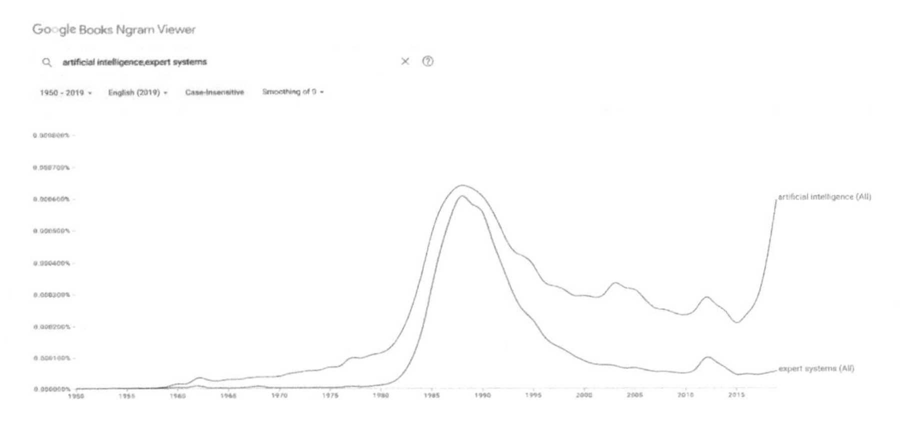

Figure 2.6. Google Ngram search for "artificial intelligence" and "expert systems"[32]

This relationship isn't mere coincidence. In actual fact, the sudden surge in usage of the term artificial intelligence at that time was caused by the rise and fall of interest in expert systems. In fact, usage in books of "artificial intelligence" only slightly outpaced that of "expert systems," as indicated by the small gap between the curve for the former and the curve for the latter during that period of time.

So what are expert systems, then, and what do they have to do with AI? The term "**expert systems**" refers to AI programs that use predefined rules and knowledge bases in a specific field in order to mimic the decisions that human experts in that field would make. As you know by

32. Ibid.

now, this makes expert systems a classic case of symbolic AI, or classical AI. Expert systems also typically feature an interface that lets users input information in order to receive direction from the program about how to handle a particular case or situation. In other words, they're decision support systems, and they were all the rage in the 1980s.

For example, in 1980, at the very beginning of the expert systems wave, Digital Equipment Corporation (DEC) implemented a rules-based system called R1, also referred to internally as XCON, a short form of the name "eXpert CONfigurer." According to John McDermott of Carnegie-Mellon University, the lead developer on the project, the purpose of R1 was to help DEC fulfill customer orders for computers:

> *R1's domain of expertise is configuring Digital Equipment Corporation's VAX-11/780 systems. Its input is a customer's order and its output is a set of diagrams displaying spatial relationships among the components on the order; these diagrams are used by the technician who physically assembles the system.*[33]

In his paper, which won the Association for the Advancement of Artificial Intelligence (AIII) Classic Paper Award in 1999, McDermott went on to describe how the typical VAX-11/780 system contained about 90 different components, such as cabinets, peripheral devices, drivers,

33. John P. McDermott, "RI: an Expert in the Computer Systems Domain." *AAAI Conference on Artificial Intelligence* (1980).

and cables, with many rules about how these components can be used together. Here is his own assessment of the performance and impact of his program:

> *The configurations that it produces are consistently adequate, and the information that it makes available to the technicians who physically assemble systems is far more detailed than that produced by the humans who do the task.*[34]

Other expert systems were developed in the 1980s to help humans make better decisions in other manufacturing environments, as well as in medical diagnoses, financial investment decisions, geology and mineral exploration, and more contexts. I distinctly recall when my own father, Richard Jones, who founded a software company in California in 1986 called Bethany Computer Systems, excitedly told me about the program he was creating for a client that would help them determine how many boxes needed to be loaded onto delivery trucks, and in what order, so as to minimize driving distance and load-unload times.

As the line in Figure 2.6 shows, though, the usage of the term "expert systems" declined starting in the late 1980s, and this drop continued throughout the decade of the 1990s. During that same time, the usage of the term "artificial intelligence" decreased as well. This decline of expert systems coincides with what many consider to be the second AI winter, starting around 1990 and extending to the early 2000s.

34. Ibid.

So what happened? Why did expert systems fade? There are a few reasons. One is that expert systems were hyper-specific and somewhat brittle. You could use an expert system to make a decision in one and only one domain, and only until the environment in that domain shifted enough to make the program obsolete. In other words, they didn't generalize well, and they tended to need constant updating, which proved to be expensive. Even John McCarthy criticized expert systems as early as 1984, when he wrote, "hardly any of them have certain *common-sense* knowledge and ability possessed by any non-feeble minded human."[35]

Another interesting perspective about why expert systems might have fallen out of favor, though, is that they worked well enough to suffer from the AI effect we discussed in the previous chapter. As a result of their usefulness, they ceased to be thought of as artificial intelligence, and they became simply software. My guess is that this is partly true, as much software today includes rules and knowledge bases that have been compiled by subject matter experts in order to aid and facilitate decision-making. The approach itself didn't totally disappear, but the marketing and branding associated with it did.

For example, earlier in my own career, I helped to design and implement a program for a medical device company in 2010 that performed a similar function as McDermott's R1 did for DEC. Our program helped assembly workers

35. J. McCarthy, "Some Expert Systems Need Common Sense, *Annals of the New York Academy of Sciences* 426 (1984): 129–137, https://doi.org/10.1111/j.1749-6632.1984.tb16516.x

disassemble and then reassemble returned insulin pumps using the most cost-effective combination of new and refurbished components available to them in inventory at any given moment on the production floor.

The configuration table of allowable combinations of different components and their many revisions had become quite bloated over time. Assembly workers, needing to make quick decisions in order to meet their productivity goals, simply didn't have enough time to flip through the documentation at their work stations. Even if they did have time to do so, it would've been very difficult for them to figure out the most cost-effective combination to use in a given work order.

Our program took into consideration the components of the disassembled pump (via barcode scan), determined which components needed to be discarded due to obsolescence, and then told the assembly worker the most cost-effective components to take out of inventory to use in the rebuild of the refurbished pump. Only an expert electrical engineer working for the company could've given the worker those same instructions, and even they would've struggled to do so.

The project saved the company millions of dollars in its first year, but it needed to be updated every time the company's engineers released a new version of any one of the pump's electronic components. The program we built, then, could be thought of as an expert system, but it was 2010, and we never once referred to what we were creating using that term, nor did we think of it as artificial intelligence. We just thought of it as a useful computer program.

There is definitely some truth to both of these reasons for the decline of popularity of expert systems – both their brittleness as well as their usefulness. But I believe we can find a third reason: the ascent of neural networks.

The Ascent of Neural Networks

If we take a look at a third version of the Google Books Ngram Viewer, as shown in Figure 2.7, we notice that at the same time the term "expert systems" was decreasing in appearance in books, another term was steadily increasing in usage: "neural networks." Furthermore, this third term closely matches the curve for "artificial intelligence" from the time it surpassed "expert systems" in usage until 2019, when the current data for Ngram stops.

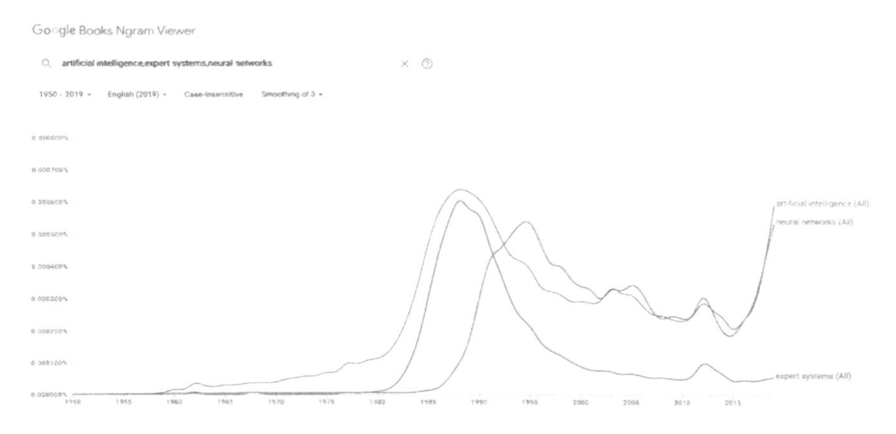

Figure 2.7. Google Books Ngram Viewer for three related terms[36]

36. Google Books Ngram Viewer, http://books.google.com/ngrams

We'll get a chance to consider the technological aspects of **artificial neural networks** (or, just **neural networks**) in more depth in the next section of this book. But for now, I'll simply say that they're a form of computational model that was originally inspired by the structure and function of the human brain, designed to adjust to patterns in data through interconnected layers of artificial neurons. To drastically oversimplify, the human brain contains something like 100 billion neurons, cells that communicate with each other by passing along electrical signals based on various stimuli. The strength of the connections between neighboring neurons can change over time as a result of our experiences, allowing us to learn, change, and grow.

In a related way, the weights between connected artificial neurons in a neural network are adjusted during the training process, and neural networks are thus said to "learn" how to perform a task from real-world data, rather than from explicit, predetermined rules. At present, neural networks are the quintessential implementation of subsymbolic AI, or connectionist AI, and they've become the dominant paradigm in artificial intelligence today. Before considering them in more detail, let's consider where they came from.

As I was taking you on a tour through the history of AI, I purposefully left out a number of influential developments that happened along the way. The reason I did so is that these developments were part of the subsymbolic branch of AI that was relegated to a backseat role in the first few decades of the history of the field.

It's not that these developments in subsymbolic AI were totally ignored; we can certainly find plenty of evidence of media hype about them, too. Rather, many of the early pioneers of AI came to feel that not much would ever come of them. As it has turned out, though, the individuals behind these early developments in subsymbolic AI were setting the stage, little by little, for the recent breakthroughs in AI. They created simple technologies that have evolved into the powerful AI implementations that are revolutionizing our world today.

Neural networks, as you recall, were a featured topic in the Dartmouth workshop at the very beginning of the field of AI, back in 1956. In his proposal for the workshop, John McCarthy referred to them as "neuron nets." Even though they were there from the beginning, they fell out of favor fairly quickly following the workshop, as the founders of the field instead focused on the rules-based approaches of symbolic AI that we've been considering so far.

Around the same time, a person who wasn't in attendance at the Dartmouth workshop was planting the seeds of the present "AI boom." In the late 1950s, a young American psychologist by the name of Frank Rosenblatt was working at the Cornell Aeronautical Laboratory in Buffalo, New York under the support of the Office of U.S. Naval Research.

While there, in 1957, he developed the **perceptron**, a model of a brain that, in his own words, "consists of a set of signal generating units (or 'neurons') connected together to form a network." It was an implementation of a 1943 invention by neuroscientists Warren McCulloch and Walter Pitts, who laid the groundwork for the use of artificial neurons in Turing machines in their seminal paper, "A Logical Calculus of the Ideas Immanent in Nervous Activity."[37]

Rosenblatt's perceptron was the first actual implementation of an artificial neural network, and it was capable of being trained to learn from data. His goal was not the same as those in the field of AI. He simply wanted to create a device that could be used to model and investigate the kind of structures found in the human brain. Referring to himself in the third person, he wrote the following:

> *For this writer, the perceptron program is not primarily concerned with the invention of devices for "artificial intelligence," but rather with investigating the physical structures and neurodynamic properties which underlie "natural intelligence." A perceptron is first and foremost a brain model, not an invention for pattern recognition."*[38]

In 1958, Rosenblatt performed a demonstration for the news media in which he fed an IBM 704 mainframe a series

37. W. S. McCulloch, S. Warren, and W. Pitts, "A logical calculus of the ideas immanent in nervous activity," *Bulletin of Mathematical Biophysics* 5 (4, 1943): 115–133, doi:10.1007/BF02478259. ISSN 1522-9602

38. F. Rosenblatt, *Principles of Neurodynamics: Perceptrons and the Theory of Brain Mechanisms* (Washington DC: Spartan Books, 1962), http://catalog.hathitrust.org/Record/000203591, https://hdl.handle.net/2027/mdp.39015039846566

of punch cards, some with holes on the left, and others with holes on the right. The mainframe was loaded with software that simulated his perceptron. The program he demonstrated was very basic by today's standards, including perhaps a few dozen artificial neurons arranged in a single layer. After fifty trials, the program became capable of distinguishing between these two different types of cards, in spite of the fact that it hadn't received any explicit instructions about how to do so.

The news media had a field day. The *Oklahoma Times* ran a story with the headline, "Frankenstein Monster Designed by Navy: Robot That Thinks." The *New York Times* had this to say in an article titled "New Navy Device Learns by Doing":

> *The Navy revealed the embryo of an electronic computer today that it expects will be able to walk, talk, see, write, reproduce itself, and be conscious of its existence....The service said it would use this principle to build the first of its Perceptron thinking machines that will be able to read and write. It is expected to be finished in about a year at a cost of $100,000.*[39]

Note that $100,000 in 1958 dollars translates to just over $1 million in 2024 funds when accounting for inflation. Once again, however, the timeline provided was overly aggressive by a long shot, and as the inevitable challenges to the expanded usage of the perceptron proved too

39. "New Navy Device Learns by Doing," *New York Times*, July 8, 1958, https://nyti.ms/41I9p3L

difficult to solve right away, enthusiasm eventually dried up.

A decade later, Minsky and Papert nearly delivered a death blow to neural networks, still in their infancy, when they shared their "intuitive judgment" that work on extending the perceptron from a single layer of neurons to multiple layers would prove to be "sterile."[40] Yikes!

As we'll consider in detail in Chapter 4, Minsky and Papert's intuition about the possibilities of multilayer neural networks proved to be wrong. Very wrong. While their 1969 book, *Perceptrons*, "is attributed with single-handedly destroying this early excitement and enthusiasm,"[41] research into neural networks continued in the background of AI. Further advancements in neural networks pushed connectionism back into the spotlight. Frank Rosenblatt wouldn't survive to see his life's work vindicated; he tragically died in a boating accident in Chesapeake Bay on his 43rd birthday, July 11, 1971.

In the interest of expediency, I'll provide a partial list of some of the milestones in the history of neural networks that followed Rosenblatt's perceptron. Entire books have been written (and in some cases, award-winning documentaries have been made!) about the following breakthroughs.

40. M. Minsky and S. Papert, *Perceptrons* (Cambridge, MA: MIT Press, 1969).
41. John D. Kelleher, *Deep Learning* (Cambridge, MA: MIT Press), 2019.

1979: Fukushima's Neocognitron

In 1979, Japanese computer scientist Kunihiko Fukushima invented the **neocognitron**, a multilayered neural network that could be trained to recognize a feature in an image no matter where the feature was located: in the top left corner, the bottom right corner, or anywhere else in the image. It was used to recognize handwritten Japanese characters.

1989: LeCun's LeNet

In 1989, French computer scientist Yann LeCun, then of Bell Labs and currently chief AI scientist of Facebook's Meta, proposed a neural network architecture called a **convolutional neural network** (**CNN, or "ConvNet"**), which was inspired by Fukushima's neocognitron. His invention, cleverly called "LeNet," employed a technique called **backpropagation** to aid in the recognition of handwritten zip codes.[42]

Conceptually, backpropagation is a method that takes the error in the output of a multilayered neural network and goes back through the network, layer by layer, adjusting the weights of each neuron to reduce the overall error of the network.

42. Y. LeCun, B. Boser, J. S. Denker, D. Henderson, R. E. Howard, W. Hubbard, and L. D. Jackel, Backpropagation Applied to Handwritten Zip Code Recognition. *Neural Computation* 1 (4, 1989): 541–551, doi: https://doi.org/10.1162/neco.1989.1.4.541

2009: Fei-Fei Li's ImageNet

While at Princeton, Chinese-born American AI researcher Fei-Fei Li began building a massive database of labeled photographs for the training of computer vision models in 2006. She employed Amazon's Mechanical Turk to task humans on the internet with providing labels for objects included in each image, such as "airplane," "cat," and "dog." In 2009, Li and her collaborators presented the initial version of the ImageNet database, which contained 3.2 million images at that point.[43] It has since grown to over 14 million images.

In 2010, following a lackluster initial reception of her database, she kicked off the ImageNet Large Scale Visual Recognition Challenge (ILSVRC), an annual competition to detect and accurately classify objects in a trimmed set of 1,000 images included in the ImageNet database. This turned out to be a stroke of genius, as the competition brought widespread attention to ImageNet, and, more importantly, to the methods employed by some of the competition's winners over the years. The impact of ImageNet and ILSVRC on the evolution of neural networks cannot be overstated, as the promotion of the usage of "big data" in the training process led to significant advances in their capabilities.

43. J. Deng, W. Dong, R. Socher, L. -J. Li, Kai Li and Li Fei-Fei, "ImageNet: A large-scale hierarchical image database," *2009 IEEE Conference on Computer Vision and Pattern Recognition,* Miami, FL, USA, 2009, pp. 248-255, doi: 10.1109/CVPR.2009.5206848.

2012: Krizhevsky's AlexNet

For example, on September 30, 2012, University of Toronto graduate student Alex Krizhevsky, working with fellow student Ilya Sutskever under the guidance of Geoffrey Hinton, won the ILSVRC with an eight-layer neural network that had 60 million weights. It was aptly named **AlexNet**, and it can be described as a variation of LeCun's LeNet in that it also featured several layers of convolutional neural networks and employed backpropagation in its training.

AlexNet didn't just win; it destroyed the competition. Its error rate was 15.3%, more than 10 percentage points lower than the second-place winner. The success of AlexNet has been credited with igniting a wave of interest in deep neural networks. Their 2012 paper, "ImageNet Classification with Deep Convolutional Neural Networks," has been cited over 147,000 times on Google Scholar to date.[44]

2016: DeepMind's AlphaGo

In 2016, Google's AI subsidiary DeepMind achieved a significant milestone in AI many years ahead of expectations. Its program **AlphaGo** defeated South Korean Lee Sedol by a score of 4–1 in a televised five-game match of the ancient Chinese strategy board game Go. This was a significant achievement for AI because Go, with its 19-by-19 playing grid, has been calculated to have 2.1×10^{170} legal board positions, a number that's far greater than the

44. Alex Krizhevsky, Ilya Sutskever, and Geoffrey E. Hinton, "ImageNet Classification with Deep Convolutional Neural Networks." *Advances in Neural Information Processing Systems* 25 (2012).

number of atoms in the observable universe, which has been estimated to be on the order of 10^{80}.[45]

Because of Go's massive number of potential board positions, the "brute force" approach employed by IBM's Deep Blue to defeat Garry Kasparov in chess in 1997, with its extensive database of moves and rapid search capabilities, simply isn't a feasible approach. The game of Go, as a result, was seen as a far greater challenge for AI than chess.

To approach this challenge, DeepMind used a system of 12 convolutional neural networks that they trained on game play using a process called **reinforcement learning (RL)**. Reinforcement learning is one of the main approaches of machine learning in which the model learns over various steps, or moves, by being given rewards for successful decisions that it makes. As a result, a neural network can be trained to achieve a goal, such as winning a complex game like Go.

The match against Sedol, widely considered to be one of the best Go players at the time, was watched by millions of viewers around the world. The result came as a shock to Sedol and his fans, and it surprised most experts in the field of AI, who felt that a victory in the game of Go was many years away due to its sheer number of possible moves. AlphaGo's victory triggered immediate surges in interest

45. John Tromp and Gunnar Farneback, "Combinatorics of Go." Computers and Games. CG 2006. Lecture Notes in Computer Science, vol 4630. Springer, Berlin, Heidelberg. https://doi.org/10.1007/978-3-540-75538-8_8

and investment in neural network research, with the government of South Korea announcing a $863 million AI fund in the aftermath of AlphaGo's victory.

2022: OpenAI's ChatGPT

On November 30, 2022, AI research organization OpenAI released an AI chatbot to the world called ChatGPT. Upon launch, ChatGPT was free to everyone, and it used OpenAI's GPT-3.5 model. GPT stands for Generative Pre-trained Transformer, and it's a **large language model (LLM)** that uses the **transformer**, a type of neural network architecture trained on a vast corpus of text from books and websites to generate humanlike text responses based on prompts submitted by users.

To say that the ChatGPT platform was a success out of the gate would be a drastic understatement. The platform achieved 100 million users by January 2023, just two months later, faster than any other software application in history. In March 2023, OpenAI released a paid subscription called ChatGPT Plus that used its next model, GPT-4, and they added functionality throughout the year, such as web search, voice, and image capabilities, as well as plugins that access third-party services such as online travel agencies and shopping sites.

The launch of ChatGPT triggered a tsunami of interest in AI around the world, but it also led to increased concerns and reservations about the negative impacts of AI, both real and potential. From copyright infringement lawsuits to claims of perpetuation of social biases to discussions about job losses and even the existential threat to the human species supposedly posed by AI, the buzz, hype, and fearmongering around AI reached a higher level than ever before. Will this hype lead to yet another AI winter? Time will tell.

Summary

Hopefully you feel that you know AI a little better now that you've taken a quick tour through the history of the field. You've become acquainted with the cyclical pattern of interest and apathy in AI, and you've learned about the splits and branches in the field, specifically the divide between symbolic AI and subsymbolic AI.

I've tried to introduce you to a handful of the more influential pioneers of the field of AI along the way, and I've pointed to some of the technologies that have pushed the field forward to where we are today. You can refer to Figure 2.8 for a summary timeline showing some of the main milestones in the history of the field of AI.

Now it's time for us to dive deeper into those technologies, especially those in the subsymbolic branch of AI. The data-driven technologies of subsymbolic AI are behind many of the recent advances we've considered, from computer vision to natural language processing to generative AI. Our understanding of AI hinges on our appreciation of machine learning and a special subset of machine learning called deep learning.

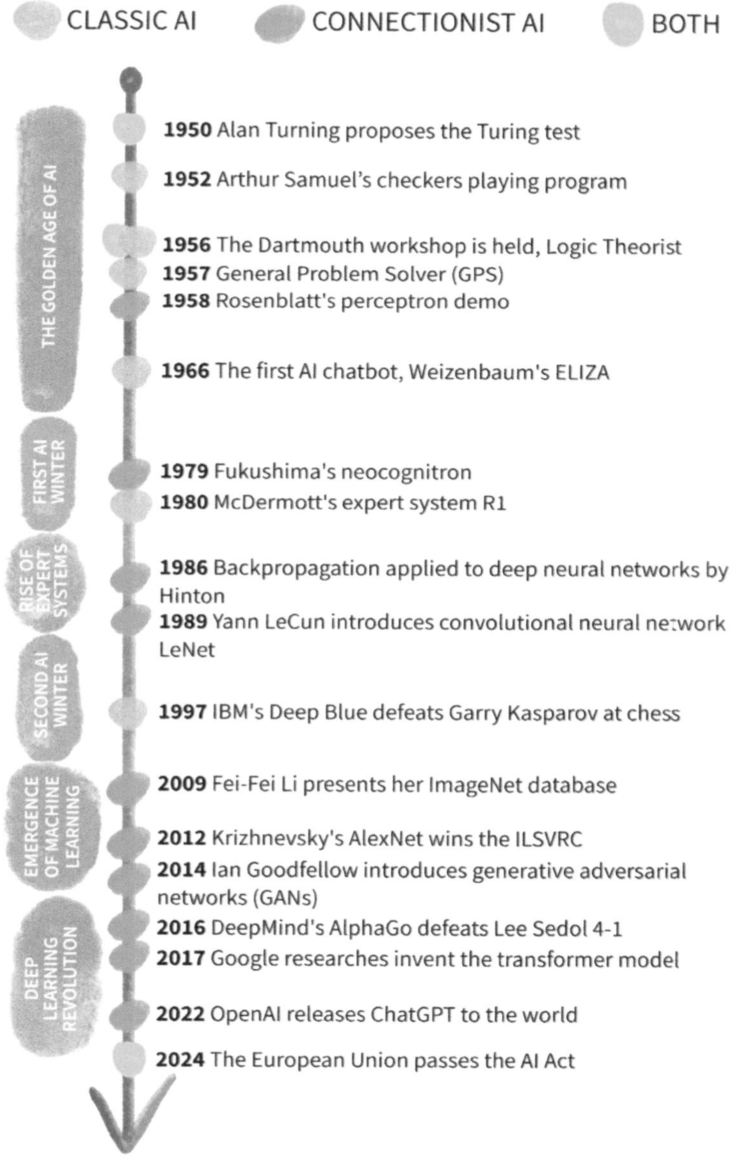

Figure 2.8. An abbreviated timeline of the history of AI

PART 2

AI Technologies

CHAPTER 3

Machine Learning Basics

"What we want is a machine that can learn from experience."
– Alan Turing, Lecture to the London Mathematical Society, February 20, 1947

In the previous chapter, we went on a journey through the history of AI, from its earliest days of relatively simple puzzle solvers to its present day manifestation of powerful technologies that interact with us and do work for us in the real world, with all of its noise and ambiguity. There's no doubt that the field of AI has come a long way in the seven decades since the Dartmouth workshop, even if it still has a long way to go for it to realize its full potential. Indeed, even knowing what AI's full potential looks like is a long way off. There are so many paths it could take.

As we considered, growth and advancement in AI has not been linear and smooth in nature. Instead, we compared change in AI to the seasons: springs and summers of enthusiasm and advancement, and winters of apathy and even retraction. But another way to think of the history of AI we've just considered is to compare it to the evolution of a living species.

Similar to the idea of punctuated equilibrium in evolutionary biology, AI has experienced periods of stagnation in which its very survival was in question, and it has also experienced sudden and dramatic leaps forward in abilities. These big leaps, like punctuated "bursts," have been driven by a series of technological breakthroughs that were made possible by important shifts in the environment.

In this chapter, we'll consider an entire family of such breakthroughs that can be found at the core of modern AI: machine learning (ML).

Basic Terms and Concepts

Machine learning (ML) is an umbrella term describing the study and use of different types of statistical algorithms that we can apply to data sets in order to learn from the patterns in those data sets how to accomplish specific tasks. When we apply a machine learning algorithm to a data set to learn its patterns, we say that we are training a model.

The data set we use for training purposes could be any group of items, in digital form, from the real world: a bunch of image files, e-books or other digital documents, audio files of people talking, spreadsheets of historical stock prices – the list of possibilities is endless. In machine learning, the data sets are typically very large. The more data, the better. We're not talking about a dozen digital photographs here; we're talking about thousands or even millions of them. Of course the training data set does not include all of the possible items; it's a sample, not an entire population. The point is that the model will learn from the sample data how to work with items that *aren't* in the sample.

The **algorithm** is the set of instructions that the program follows in the training process. It's like a recipe of sorts, a step-by-step procedure to learn from the training data. There are different kinds of machine learning algorithms, from neural networks to decision trees to various clustering algorithms, and we'll consider some of them in this book.

The **model** is what results from the training process; it's a trained algorithm. The model has specific **parameters** that have been adjusted during the training process – like dials or knobs on an old AM/FM radio that you turn to fine-tune the signal and the sound. These adjustments that the algorithm makes to the model during training allow the model to perform its task at a certain level of accuracy, though never quite perfectly.

For example, let's say you want to create a program that can tell what numbers someone has written by hand on a personal check they want to deposit into their bank account using their smartphone. The program will need to, among other tasks, convert a digital photograph of the check into an amount to deposit along with a bank account number and a routing number. It turns out that using machine learning will give you much better results than if you try to just tell the program what to do. How would the program handle the many different handwriting styles we all have, not to mention the quality, angle, and lighting conditions of the photograph?

Rather than trying to come up with instructions on your own, you could instead train a convolutional neural network (CNN) algorithm by giving it many different digital photographs of checks with handwritten numbers. The resulting CNN model would have fine-tuned parameters called **weights** that would yield a certain level of accuracy when you give it images of checks that weren't in its training data set. With enough training data, and with the right machine learning algorithm, it's remarkable what the resulting model can do. That's an example of machine learning.

Historical Context of Machine Learning

The term "machine learning" was coined in the 1950s by Arthur Samuel, the American AI pioneer whose checkers-player was one of the very first examples of a program that exhibited self-learning. It did so by adjusting its internal scoring system as it played more and more games of checkers, resulting in improvements in its choices of moves over time.

If you think about it, it makes sense that the ability to learn would become such an important aspect of artificial intelligence. It's how the definition of intelligence itself begins: "the ability to learn or understand or to deal with new or trying situations."[46] Taking in one's surroundings, figuring out what's going on, and then adjusting accordingly to improve one's outcomes: these abilities are a huge part of what it means to be intelligent, both for humans and for computers.

The data-based approach of machine learning is the essence of subsymbolic AI, and it stands in contrast to the rules-based approach at the heart of symbolic AI. If the field of AI were a pendulum, then it started on the side of symbolic AI in the 1950s, and it swung to the side of subsymbolic AI and machine learning in the late 1990s to early-2000s, where it has been ever since. AI in the early days of the 21st century has been all about learning. Where will it go from here? We'll see.

As a discipline, machine learning hasn't always been such a cozy cohabitant of the overall "house" of AI, with its various rooms and roommates. At various points in time, experts in the field of machine learning have thought of themselves as separate from the field of AI, and vice versa. I imagine that these sentiments have mostly arisen due to differences in respective areas of focus, and maybe even some competition for funding and credit.

46. *Merriam-Webster.com Dictionary*, s.v. "intelligence," https://www.merriam-webster.com/dictionary/intelligence. Accessed January 29, 2024.

The hybrid acronym "AI/ML" has even surfaced recently to refer to artificial intelligence that has a focus on machine learning techniques. Some find this acronym to be a helpful way to indicate the connection, but others find it to be unnecessary and even confusing. I'm of the opinion that machine learning is a subfield within the broader field of AI, so, at the moment anyway, I don't see a hybrid acronym as adding much value to the conversation.

If you think about it, the most primitive forms of machine learning were right there at the very beginning of AI. Arthur Samuel's checkers-playing program and Frank Rosenblatt's perceptron were both created in the 1950s, during the golden age of AI. So why did more than three decades have to pass before machine learning became such a dominant paradigm in AI? Part of the answer is that the environmental conditions needed to shift in a way that would enable the ascendance of machine learning.

Factor #1: Increasing AI Compute

One environmental condition that has changed continuously over the decades is computational power and speed, also known as **AI compute,** or sometimes just called **compute**. According to Moore's law, named after Intel co-founder Gordon Moore, the number of components that can fit on an integrated circuit has doubled every year since around 1975.[47] In addition, the more recent application

47. Roser, Max, Hannah Ritchie, and Edouard Mathieu. "What is Moore's Law?" Our World in Data, March 28, 2023, https://ourworldindata.org/moores-law

of **graphics processing units (GPUs)** to the training of machine learning models – especially the training of deep neural networks, which we'll consider in the next chapter – has led to dramatic improvements in the performance of those models.[48]

GPUs are a special type of computer chip designed to perform the rapid mathematical calculations required to render rich 3D graphics in fast-paced modern video games. In a classic case of repurposing one tool for a different use, AI researchers have found ways to use multiple GPUs in parallel to train machine learning models, allowing them to create more and more complex AI programs.

Without these significant increases in computational power, it seems unlikely that machine learning would've taken off like it did. As a result of how useful GPUs are in the training of machine learning models, companies that produce them such as NVIDIA have seen enormous sales growth associated with the adoption of generative AI tools like ChatGPT.

Factor #2: Availability of Training Data

Compute isn't the only environmental factor that has fueled the acceleration of machine learning, though. In order to be trained to perform specific tasks, machine learning models need data – lots of it. The amount of data that's readily

48. "AI and Compute." OpenAI, May 16, 2018, https://openai.com/research/ai-and-compute. Accessed 11 January 2024.

available to use to train machine learning algorithms has increased dramatically along with adoption of the internet and mobile phones. Users of social media platforms that have risen in popularity since the turn of the 21st century have uploaded massive amounts of data to the internet in the form of text, images, audio, and video.

It's not just social media. Authors have published e-books, journalists have published web articles, academics have published research papers in PDF form, and older books, articles, and papers have been digitized, too. On top of all that, internet users have interacted with each other on a daily basis on message boards like Reddit, carrying on conversations about a dizzying array of topics.

Much of this content has been scraped from the web and compiled into data repositories like **Common Crawl** that have been used to train and fine-tune the powerful machine learning algorithms we use today. Other repositories like Fei-Fei Li's ImageNet have been created with the explicit purpose of furthering the development of machine learning models. Where would machine learning be without all of this rich data on which to train? I don't know, but we can say that it simply wouldn't be where it is today, at the forefront of AI.

We can't consider the importance of these massive repositories of data without also acknowledging their many thorny issues, such as dirty data, copyrights, privacy, and social bias. These issues and others raise ethical and legal concerns about the use of machine learning models trained on problematic data, and we'll consider such objections in Chapter 5.

The Three Major Forms of Machine Learning

For now, I'd like to touch on the different ways machine learning algorithms themselves can learn from data. Just as you and I can learn in different ways based on the situation we find ourselves in, machine learning algorithms can learn in different ways, too. Sometimes we find ourselves in a classroom, learning from a teacher. Other times we find ourselves out in the world, learning from patterns we notice around us. Still other times we find ourselves performing some activity that's new to us, learning how to do it by a process of trial and error.

These three different types of real-world situations mirror the three major forms of machine learning: **supervised learning**, **unsupervised learning**, and **reinforcement learning**. Each of these types of learning is useful in different situations, and for achieving different objectives.

SUPERVISED LEARNING

A model is trained on data that a human "supervisor" has labeled with the correct answer.

It's like someone labeling pictures of a bike as "right" and everything else as "wrong."

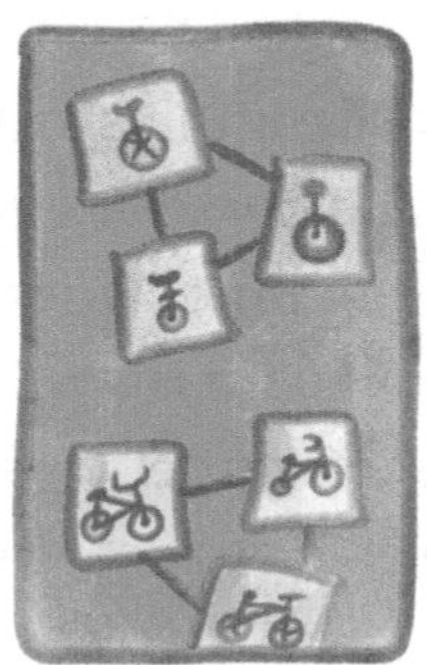

UNSUPERVISED LEARNING

A model is trained to find patterns in data that has not been labeled with any correct answer.

It's like a model finds patterns to identify types of bikes and groups them together.

REINFORCEMENT LEARNING

A model is trained by being given rewards and penalties as it interacts with an environment.

It's like someone learning how to ride a bike through trial-and-error.

Figure 3.1. The three major forms of machine learning

In this chapter, we'll consider them one by one. In a nutshell, supervised learning is like when we learn from a teacher which answers are right and which are wrong; unsupervised learning is like when we learn for ourselves by observing patterns around us; and reinforcement learning is like when we learn by doing, figuring it out gradually by the feedback we get from our attempts. Let's consider these differing forms of machine learning one by one.

Supervised Learning

The first and perhaps most common type of machine learning is known as **supervised learning**. The goal of supervised learning is to teach a model how to reliably and accurately convert inputs into their associated correct outputs. What are the inputs and what are the outputs? It depends on the purpose of the program. Maybe the inputs are photographs of automobiles going through an intersection, and the outputs are the license plate numbers to be used to identify the owner to send them a ticket for failing to stop at a red light. Maybe the inputs are voice commands in audio form, and the outputs are strings of text of what was actually said to the virtual assistant – maybe "play me songs by Sam Cooke."

Try to imagine writing down instructions for a computer so that it could perform these tasks at a high level of quality. For the license plate photographs, how would the program handle the wide variety of possible angles, lighting conditions, and license plate types? For the voice commands, how would the program parse out the words no matter the person's accent, speaking pace, or background noises in the room picked up by the microphone? As humans, we can usually do a pretty good job performing these tasks ourselves, but the challenge to get a computer to perform them as well as we do – or better – eluded AI researchers for a long time.

That all changed when researchers discovered that supervised learning of models, especially deep neural networks, could be used to dramatically increase the accuracy of the programs used to perform these kinds of tasks. With this approach, humans "supervise" the training of a model by giving it many pairs of inputs and their correct outputs. Instead of trying to explicitly tell a computer how to do it, they give a model lots and lots of examples of how to do it and how not to do it.

The training data is paired: the inputs have **features** and the outputs have **labels**. In the case of a digital photograph of a car going through an intersection, the features of the input are the RGB (red, green, and blue) values of every single pixel in the image, and the outputs might be the corresponding automobile license plate that appears in each image.

For each input given to the model during the training process, the model converts the input features into an output. Then it compares its output to the known correct output (the label), and then adjusts its parameters to reduce its error, which is simply the difference between the model's output and the correct output. At first, the model is just providing random guesses. After many rounds, or **epochs**, of training, its accuracy is much better than that. This is the process of training a model using supervised learning.

It's exactly what Frank Rosenblatt did back in 1958 when he demonstrated his perceptron program using an IBM 704 mainframe. The inputs were punch cards with holes on either the left or the right side that he fed into the mainframe. The outputs took the form of lights on the mainframe that the perceptron program would turn on or off to communicate its guess. Rosenblatt trained his perceptron program using the first 50 punch cards he gave it. For each of the 50 cards, it made an initial guess, and then adjusted its internal parameters if its guess was wrong.

The training data in the case of supervised learning is **labeled data**. The labels are the correct outputs, like an answer key to a test. The human providing the right answers is like the teacher, or "supervisor," and the model is like the student learning from the example questions (the inputs with their features) and their associated right answers (the outputs with their labels). Once the model has been shown many pairs of inputs and outputs, it's given a test, just like a student in a class would be tested on how well they learned. The test involves questions (inputs) that the model hasn't yet seen, and outputs that are known to the human trainer (the "supervisor"), but that are hidden from the model.

Unsupervised Learning

The next major type of machine learning is **unsupervised learning**. Again, unsupervised learning can be compared to the process we go through when we observe patterns in the world around us, all by ourselves. As with self-guided discovery, unsupervised learning doesn't involve a teacher, or "supervisor," providing the right answers. That's why it's unsupervised. According to Yann LeCun, "most of human and animal learning is unsupervised learning."[49]

In the context of unsupervised learning, training the model takes on a different meaning. There's no utilization of a separate training data set with input features matching to known output labels that the model needs to learn. Instead, the model trains on the actual, real-world data set. This data set is **unlabeled**; the inputs aren't labeled with known, correct outputs like they are in the case of supervised learning. Unsupervised learning is called "unsupervised" because the inputs in the actual data aren't labeled with any corresponding outputs. The model needs to figure out what the outputs should be, without being "supervised" by a human, who can tell the model whether its output is right or wrong. But what does this actually look like?

Think about the case of a company that wants to divide its customers into different groups that have similar attributes. This is called **customer segmentation**. The company might decide to create predefined segments based on one or more customer traits or behaviors, such as how old

49. Patel, Ankur A. *Hands-On Unsupervised Learning Using Python*. O'Reilly Media, Inc., 2019.

they are, or where they live, or the total amount of money they spent on products last year. That would be pretty straightforward, and they wouldn't need to use machine learning for that. Each customer could simply be labeled with the name of the customer segment they belong to.

But what if the company didn't have such a predefined segmentation they wanted to apply to their list of customers? What if they just wanted to know who is most similar to whom, and in what way? The marketers could apply a machine learning algorithm called **clustering** to their full list of customers. The clustering algorithm uses unsupervised learning to find groups in the data that have members that are as similar to each other as possible (this is called **maximizing intra-cluster similarity**), while at the same time being as different as possible from members of the other groups (**minimizing inter-cluster similarity**).

The algorithm uses a measure such as **Euclidean distance** to figure out how similar or different data points are from each other. To find the Euclidean distance between two data points, you find the difference between each of their corresponding values, or coordinates, square the differences, add up all the resulting squares of differences, and then take the square root of the sum. For models based on just two variables (many models contain more than two), the Euclidean distance would be the same thing as finding the length of the hypotenuse of the triangle they form, as shown in Figure 3.2.

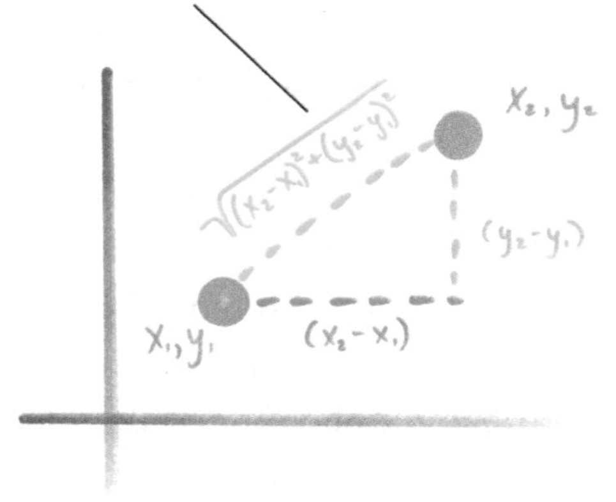

Figure 3.2. The Euclidean distance between two points

Many clustering algorithms iteratively adjust the clusters little by little in order to increase similarity *within* groups while decreasing similarity *between* groups. When the algorithm is done, the model has placed each data point into one of a number of groups. But how many clusters or segments should there be? Some clustering algorithms automatically figure this out for the user, and others, like **K-means clustering**, allow the user to specify upfront the number of clusters (K) that they want the model to have.

For example, in the K-means clustering example shown in Figure 3.3, I asked the algorithm to create five clusters of countries based on their 2020 populations, economy sizes based on Gross Domestic Product (GDP) per capita, and CO_2 emission rates based on metric tons per capita. You can see that the algorithm created a group with the two largest populations (China and India), a second group with the six highest CO_2 emitters, a third group with the 18 countries that have the highest GDP per capita (minus Qatar, which it placed in the second group instead), a fourth group with the 122 lowest emitters (minus India), and a group of 43 countries that are in the middle of both axes (minus China).

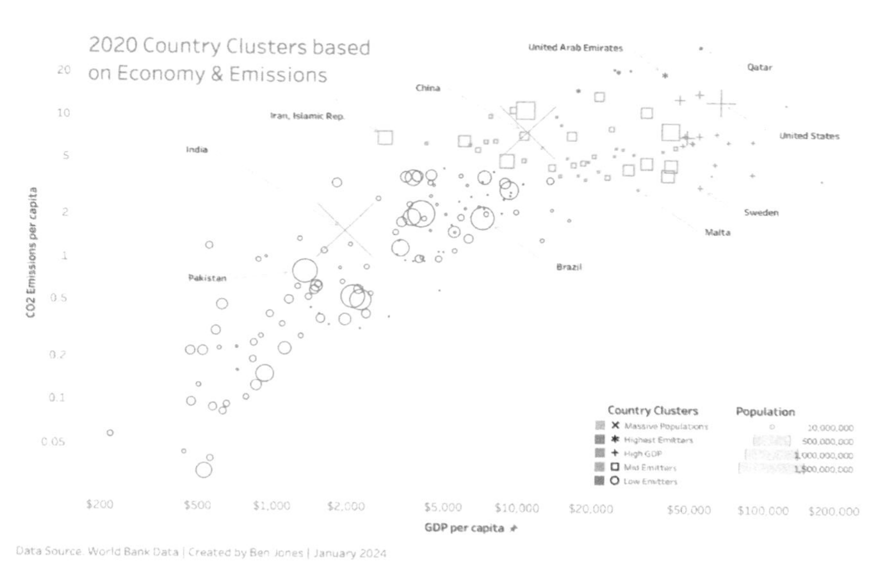

Figure 3.3. Clusters of countries based on economies and emissions

The point with unsupervised learning is to use the power of computers to find something that would be very difficult and time-consuming for a human to find by themselves: clusters that naturally occur within the data. These clusters aren't predefined by humans who want to impose some grouping scheme on their data. Instead, the clusters arise from the data itself. The model learns from the data what the clusters should be. Here, no separate training data set is needed. The model learns from the full data set itself.

Reinforcement Learning

The third major type of machine learning is called reinforcement learning. **Reinforcement learning (RL)** is learning how to do something new, involving decisions about what actions to take, particularly when each action involves feedback in the form of rewards or penalties. An AI agent interacting with the world in this way can use reinforcement learning to get better and better outcomes over time.

Think of learning to ride a bicycle. If a teacher told you a set of right answers of what to do and what not to do (like supervised learning), you wouldn't be able to go out and ride a bicycle, even if you got a perfect score on the written test. And even if you sat there all day and watched all the other kids in the neighborhood riding bicycles, carefully noticing any patterns in their movements (like unsupervised learning), you still wouldn't be able to ride a bicycle. To learn to ride a bicycle, you'd have to get on the bicycle and try to ride it. At first, you'd pedal once or twice, and then you'd probably fall over. That would hurt, and you might even skin your knee or bruise your shoulder.

Those painful experiences would be like punishments for actions that you probably shouldn't have taken. You try again, and you fall again. Eventually, you get to five or even ten pedals before falling. The rush of the wind in your hair would be exhilarating – an incredible reward for your adjustments and your improvements. You get better and better. Soon, you're riding around the neighborhood with the other kids, getting some air off of little jumps, popping a wheelie, riding with one hand on the handlebar, and then no hands. Life is good.

Our actions have consequences, and we can use these consequences to help us improve so that we can achieve our goals, even in a messy and imperfect world. We can teach computers to do this, too. A famous example is the AlphaGo program I mentioned in the previous chapter. Remember how the game of Go presented a daunting challenge for AI? Its 19-by-19 square playing surface results in too many possible moves to just put them all in a database to search and find a good move. How, then, can a computer learn how to play it so well that it could defeat even the best players in the world?

Enter AlphaGo, and reinforcement learning. First, the program's system of 12 convolutional neural networks was trained to mimic human experts. It was given a database of 30 million moves of historical games played by humans. This initial "bootstrapping" wasn't reinforcement learning, though. It was classic supervised learning. The inputs were board positions that were labeled with a known "good" move – the move actually made by the human player when the game was played sometime in the past.

After this initial phase of supervised learning, AlphaGo was pretty good at Go; it could predict the next move of the human expert 57% of the time.[50] Its creators at DeepMind, however, wanted to make it even better. So they made it play against other instances of itself. AlphaGo versus AlphaGo. Based on the outcomes of thousands of games of self-play, it continued improving its model via reinforcement learning. The weights, or parameters, of its neural networks would be adjusted based on the outcomes of the decisions it made.

When it came time to play South Korean world champion Lee Sedol, the model had improved to such a point that its strength was apparent out of the gate. It didn't just beat Sedol, it made some moves during the game that really puzzled the experts. They were, in a way, quite inhuman: very unlike the kind of move a human expert would likely make in a similar situation. The techniques that AlphaGo had learned in self-play were unlike any in the 2,500 year history of the game of Go.

The team at DeepMind also used reinforcement learning to teach AI programs how to play video games like Atari's breakout. Reinforcement learning is also important in the development of self-driving cars, as the model needs to learn from decisions it makes on the road. Other types of robots, such as those used in the factory for assembly, also

50. Silver, David, and Demis Hassabis. "AlphaGo: Mastering the Ancient Game of Go with Machine Learning." Google Research Blog, January, 27, 2016, blog.research.google/2016/01/alphago-mastering-ancient-game-of-go.html.

use reinforcement learning to improve their outcomes over time.

Recently, OpenAI used a form of reinforcement learning called **reinforcement learning from human feedback (RLHF)** in order to train and fine-tune its recent versions of its GPT large language models used in its AI chatbot ChatGPT.[51] The way it works is that human labelers look at prompts submitted by users of a sandbox version of the chatbot, and then they provide examples of desirable responses to these prompts. They also rate or rank the actual responses of the model, effectively scoring it based on how much they like the output, and whether it meets or violates specific criteria. These rankings are then used as feedback to fine-tune the model. High rankings are like rewards for the model, and low rankings are a form of punishment. In effect, the model is being trained how to provide responses that meet the preferences of the human judges.

Other Types of Machine Learning

We've considered the three main forms of machine learning: supervised learning, unsupervised learning, and reinforcement learning. There are other forms of machine learning, too. For example, **semi-supervised learning** is a combination of supervised learning and unsupervised learning. With this approach, models are trained using

51. "Instruction Following." OpenAI, https://openai.com/research/instruction-following. Accessed January 29, 2024.

a small amount of labeled data – say, a few hundred hand-categorized photographs – and then they also learn from a huge amount of unlabeled data – say, the rest of the uncategorized photographs uploaded to the social media platform.

With **self-supervised learning**, the labels of the training data set aren't provided by a human teacher or supervisor, per se. Instead, they are created by the system itself. For example, a large language model like Meta's llama or OpenAI's GPT-4 is trained to predict the next word in a sentence. The model is fed large amounts of text from books, articles, and websites, and it uses the sentences in this training data to construct tests for itself: "It was the best of times, it was the…" The model learns to give the answer: "worst," then "of," then "times," by guessing and checking the right answer in the training data. No human creates these quizzes with paired questions and answers. The algorithm goes through the body of text and automatically generates them.

Overfitting and Underfitting

No data set is perfect, and that's true of training data sets used in machine learning, too. Training data sets can contain anomalies, erroneous or inaccurate values, and plain old noise. Noise is the presence of imperfections in the data that can come from many sources, including variability in the way the data was measured, collected, or processed. In addition, a training data set might include certain details or lack other relevant details about the task to be learned, and the person using it to train their model might not be aware of it.

For example, let's say you're trying to train a model to determine if a photograph includes a dog. If your training data set only includes certain breeds of dogs, or if the dogs are all sitting or standing, then your model will learn that these aspects are statistically relevant to the task at hand. Then, if you show it a photo of a different breed of dog, or one with a dog jumping, it may not be able to identify the dog in the photo.

This is a common problem in machine learning called **overfitting**. An overfitted model has learned that the noise and the irrelevant details present in the training data are important factors to consider when carrying out the task at hand. As a result, an overfitted model will perform poorly when given data it didn't see in the training process. This scenario is shown on the right of Figure 3.4. It's represented as a shoe with too many contours to fit too precisely to someone's foot.

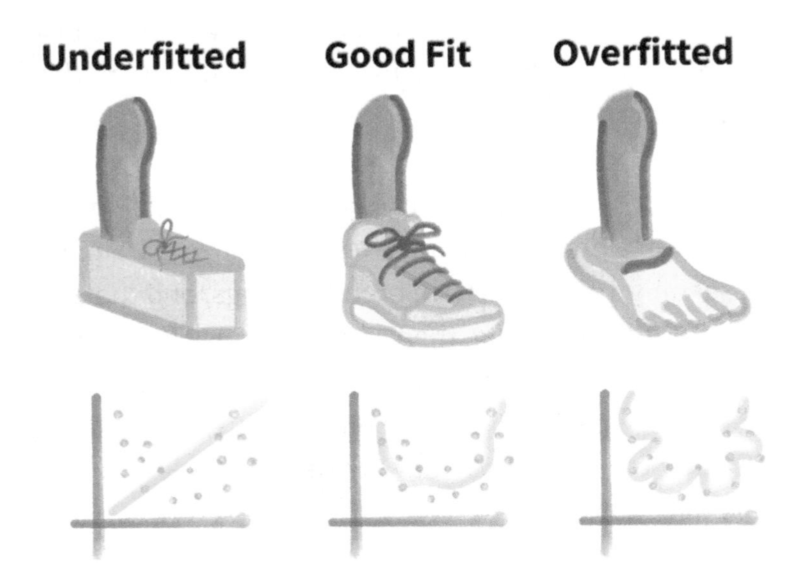

Figure 3.4. Overfitting and underfitting in machine learning

On the other hand (or, foot), **underfitting** is when the model is too simple, and doesn't learn enough of the relevant information in the training data set. It's represented on the left side of Figure 3.4 as another kind of poorly-fitting shoe: one without enough of a shape to it. An underfitted model will also perform poorly when given inputs that it hasn't seen in its training data. In the middle is the "goldilocks" case of a model that has a good fit to the data. This is, of course, what every machine learning practitioner is hoping to achieve, but it can be very elusive.

Summary

In this chapter, we touched on the basic concepts of machine learning, a critical subfield within AI and the embodiment of the branch of subsymbolic AI. We gained an appreciation for the way changes in two key environmental factors enabled the ascent of machine learning: the dramatic increases in both computational power, or compute, as well as the amount of data available to train machine learning models.

We considered various ways that humans have figured out how to give computers the ability to learn from data, and we related these different approaches to various forms of human learning. Sometimes, a teacher gives us right and wrong answers to memorize, similar to supervised learning. Other times, we have to observe our environment and find the patterns ourselves, not totally unlike unsupervised learning. And other times we actually have to try things out, make decisions, take actions, and learn from the consequences, kind of like reinforcement learning. These are just three of the many learning algorithms we find under the machine learning umbrella.

And machine learning, while sometimes thought of at the same level as AI itself, does not equate to AI. Symbolic AI is still highly relevant, even if it's having its own turn in the shadows. If the pendulum of focus has swung away from symbolic AI and all the way over to subsymbolic AI in the past few decades, then perhaps a return to balance would unlock future growth. In the next chapter, we'll consider a particularly powerful subfield within machine learning: deep learning.

CHAPTER 4

A Primer on Deep Learning

> **"The tools and technologies we've developed are really the first few drops of water in the vast ocean of what AI can do."**
> **– Fei-Fei Li, the "godmother" of AI**

We started our journey defining AI as the development of computer systems that can perform tasks typically requiring human intelligence. Then, after a brief tour through the annals of history, we focused on machine learning, which is the ability of computer programs to learn from data how to perform such tasks. Now, in this chapter, we'll take a deep dive into the world of deep learning, which is a specific kind of machine learning that has unlocked incredible capabilities in computers in recent decades.

The relationship between AI, machine learning, and deep learning is often represented as an Euler diagram, with AI as the largest circle, machine learning as the medium-sized circle contained entirely within the larger circle, and deep learning as the smallest circle contained entirely within the medium-sized circle (and therefore also entirely within the largest circle).

If you think about it, though, this relationship presents a perfect opportunity to use the Russian doll as an analogy. Deep learning is a subset of machine learning, which in turn is a subset of AI: a world within a world within a world.

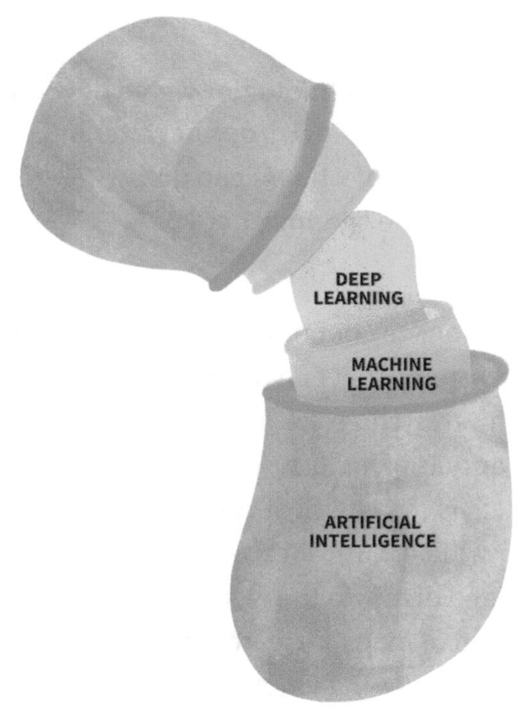

Figure 4.1. The relationship between AI, machine learning, and deep learning

What this means, of course, is that whatever classifies as deep learning also classifies as machine learning, and whatever classifies as machine learning also classifies as AI. The converse of these two statements, though, isn't necessarily true. There are some types of AI that are not machine learning (e.g. expert systems or knowledge graphs), and there are some types of machine learning that are not deep learning (e.g. decision trees or clustering).

Deep learning is a special branch of machine learning that involves a specific family of artificial neural networks: **deep neural networks (DNN)**. DNNs have changed the world of AI, and in so doing they have changed the world we live in. In 2018, deep learning experts Yann LeCun, Yoshua Bengio, and Geoffrey Hinton were joint winners of the ACM A.M. Turing Award "for conceptual and engineering breakthroughs that have made deep neural networks a critical component of computing."[52] This prestigious award is often called the Nobel Prize in Computing, even though the Association for Computing Machinery (ACM) has no affiliation with the Nobel Foundation.

In this chapter, we'll discuss what's "deep" about deep neural networks and deep learning, and why this special branch of machine learning has become so critical to AI, to computing, and indeed to society as a whole. Advances involving deep neural networks have been behind most of the breakthroughs in AI since the beginning of the 21st century. In order to gain a conceptual understanding of deep neural networks, we need to start with what originally

52. "Fathers of the Deep Learning Revolution Receive ACM A.M. Turing Award," ACM Awards. Accessed February 25, 2024, https://awards.acm.org/about/2018-turing.

inspired these powerful models: the fundamental unit of the human brain – the biological neuron.

Biological Neurons

According to current estimations, neuroscientists believe the human brain contains around 86 billion **biological neurons**.[53] Each one is a nerve cell composed of a **nucleus** that sends and receives electrical and chemical signals to and from other neighboring neurons via **synapses**, junctions between the single **axon** of the "upstream" neuron sending the signal and the many fingerlike **dendrites** of its neighboring "downstream" neurons that receive the signal. Figure 4.2 provides an artistic rendering of these main components of the biological neuron.

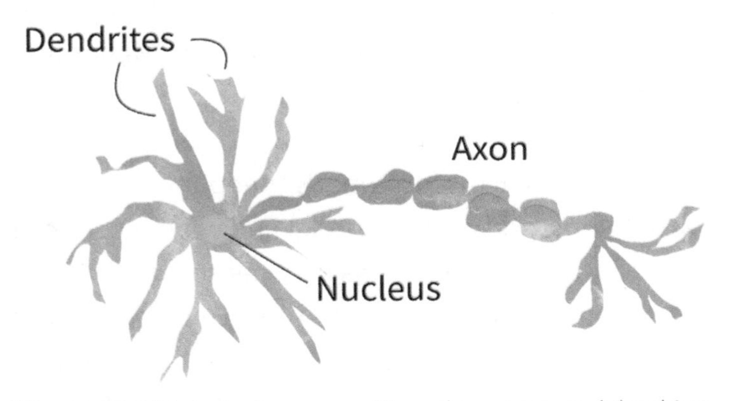

Figure 4.2. A biological neuron, with nucleus, axon, and dendrites

53. Azevedo, F.A., Carvalho, L.R., Grinberg, L.T., Farfel, J.M., Ferretti, R.E., Leite, R.E., Jacob Filho, W., Lent, R., and Herculano-Houzel, S. Equal numbers of neuronal and nonneuronal cells make the human brain an isometrically scaled-up primate brain. *J Comp Neurol* 513, no. 5 (April 10, 2009): 532–41. doi: 10.1002/cne.21974. PMID: 19226510.

In the human brain, each neuron can be connected in this way to thousands of other neurons.[54] If the combination of the input signals passed along a neuron's dendrites to its nucleus is strong enough, the neuron will "fire" an electrical signal (also called an **action potential**) along its own single axon toward the connected dendrites of neighboring cells. It's the communication between neurons, along with the brain's connection to sensory inputs and motor controls via the central nervous system, that enable us to process information and to respond to external stimuli.

A neuron can have a very strong connection with another neuron, and therefore they will often fire together. It can also have a relatively weak connection with another neuron, so that the influence the upstream neuron has on the downstream neuron isn't as great. Furthermore, the connections between individual neurons in the brain can strengthen or weaken over time based on our activities and experiences – a phenomenon known as **neuroplasticity** that plays a central role in our ability to learn and form memories.

Artificial Neurons

In somewhat similar fashion, though quite different in many ways, each **artificial neuron** in a neural network communicates with other artificial neurons to which it's connected. In practice in AI, it's common for artificial neurons to simply be called "neurons," though you may

54. Gulati, A. Understanding neurogenesis in the adult human brain. *Indian J Pharmacol* 47, no. 6 (November–December 2015): 583–84. doi: 10.4103/0253-7613.169598. PMID: 26729946; PMCID: PMC4689008.

also hear them called “simulated neurons” from time to time. To maintain clarity, henceforth in this book I’ll refer to artificial neurons as “neurons” and biological neurons as “biological neurons.” If this were a book about the human brain, I’d probably refer to biological neurons as “neurons” and artificial neurons as “artificial neurons.” It’s not a book about the human brain, though. So there you have it.

How does a neuron work? It receives a set of digital inputs, multiplies each individual input by a corresponding **weight**, adds up the resulting values (a “weighted sum”), and then plugs the weighted sum into its **activation function**, a mathematical equation that determines the output of the neuron. Once it has obtained the output of its activation function, known as its **activation**, it sends this digital signal downstream as the output or as an input to another neuron. Figure 4.3 shows a diagram of Frank Rosenblatt’s perceptron, which he created in the 1950s – the very first neuron ever created.

How did Rosenblatt’s perceptron work? It took a set of inputs from various sensors, multiplied each input by its own weight, summed up the weighted inputs, and then compared this sum to a threshold value. If the sum was less than the threshold value, the perceptron would output a value of –1. If the sum was greater than or equal to the threshold value then it would output a value of 1. For a more detailed diagram of Rosenblatt’s perceptron, including mathematical notation, see Appendix 1.

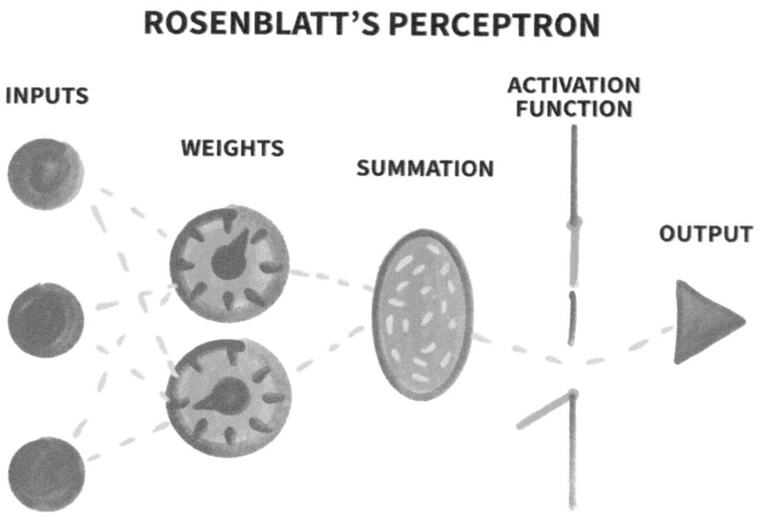

ROSENBLATT'S PERCEPTRON

INPUTS
WEIGHTS
SUMMATION
ACTIVATION FUNCTION
OUTPUT

Figure 4.3. A diagram of Frank Rosenblatt's perceptron

That's why this type of activation function is called a **threshold activation function**: the output changes all of a sudden from one binary value to the other as soon as the weighted sum of the inputs hit a specific threshold, kind of like a basic light switch. We can choose values of –1 and 1 to represent a binary output as Rosenblatt did, or we can also represent a binary output using values of 0 and 1 as people often do; both representations are valid.

But what could this simple contraption be used for, and why would we consider it to be anything close to "intelligent?" As you'll recall from our brief tour through the history of AI, Rosenblatt fed 50 punch cards, one by one, into an IBM 704 mainframe computer with his perceptron program loaded onto it. After this process, the program learned how to tell the difference between a punch card with a hole on the right side and one with a hole on the left side.

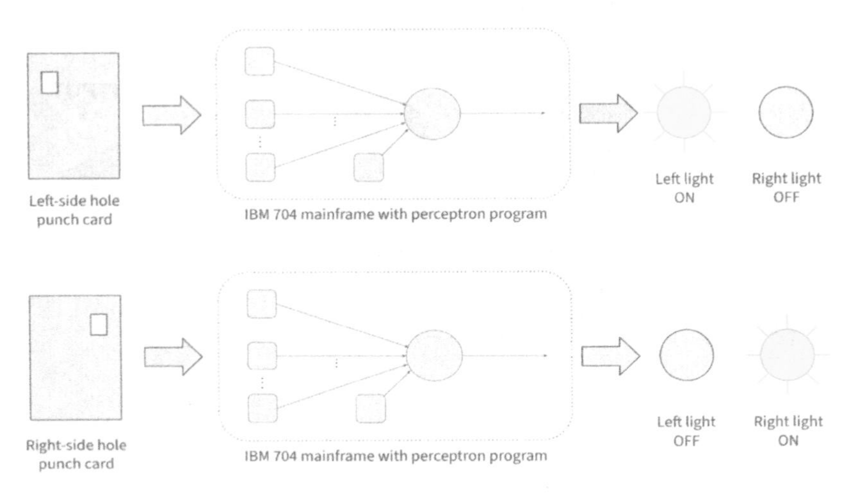

Figure 4.4. A diagram of Rosenblatt's perceptron demonstration

But how did it actually *learn*? The key is in the weights of the neuron, and in the way the weights were adjusted during the training process so as to increase the accuracy of the output. The weights of a neuron are loosely analogous to the strengths of the synaptic connections between biological neurons in the human brain. Weights with higher values are kind of like more efficient synapses: they result in an input signal exerting a bigger influence on a neuron. Increasing the value of a particular weight increases the influence of the input associated with that weight. Inversely, decreasing the value of a weight decreases the corresponding input's influence on the neuron.

The reason for this is that every input to a neuron is multiplied by a specific weight. You can think of it like turning each input's volume up or down. If an input's corresponding weight gets increased during training, then the input's "volume" goes up and it has more of an influence on the neuron. If that same input's weight gets decreased during training, then the input's "volume" goes down and it has less of an influence on the neuron. It turns out that it's possible to adjust the weights of a neuron little by little during training so that the neuron is more likely to produce an output that's correct, or desirable.

Okay, but how, exactly, did Rosenblatt's perceptron adjust its own weights during training? At first, the weights of the perceptron were randomly determined. Then Rosenblatt fed a punch card into the mainframe and the perceptron produced a binary output that would turn on one light for a guess of "left-side hole," and would turn on a different light for a guess of "right-side hole."

Here's the kicker: if the perceptron guessed *correctly*, the perceptron's weights would stay the same. But if it guessed *incorrectly*, its weights would be adjusted by a simple formula that would effectively reduce the error in the output. The error is a function of the difference between the actual output and the expected (correct) output. The new, adjusted weights reduced the error, meaning the perceptron would be more likely to produce the correct output for that specific punch card.

After going through this process with different cards 50 times, the weights of the perceptron had been adjusted to values that enabled it to give an accurate guess. The perceptron had "learned" how to differentiate between punch cards with holes on the left side and those with holes on the right side. You know by now that this type of machine learning is supervised learning, because a "supervisor" – in this case, Rosenblatt – told the model during each training run whether its output was correct or incorrect.

The principles behind today's neurons are remarkably similar to those of Rosenblatt's original creation, albeit with a few very important differences. First, the inputs and outputs of a modern neuron aren't typically binary. Instead, they can take a continuous range of values, like a light with a dimmer switch instead of a simple on/off switch. This contributes to their ability to solve nonbinary problems that are much more complex than figuring out whether a punch card has a hole on the left side or the right side.

Second, modern neurons rarely use threshold activation functions, mostly due to their abrupt jumps that result in sharp edges, sometimes called discontinuities. Instead, researchers have found that smoother activation functions enable the training of vastly more complex networks, which we'll consider in a moment. See Appendix 2 for a diagram of a modern artificial neuron.

Neural Networks

While Rosenblatt's perceptron program that he demonstrated in the 1950s only included a single perceptron, today's AI programs don't have just one single neuron; they include many neurons arranged in a network. A simple **feedforward neural network** is shown in Figure 4.5 (see Appendix 3 for a more detailed diagram).

This type of neural network is called feedforward because all of the connections point forward in the same direction, from the left side to the right side of the diagram. No connections point in the opposite direction, from the right to the left, and no loopbacks or cycles exist within the network. Information is "fed" in only one direction: from the inputs toward the outputs.

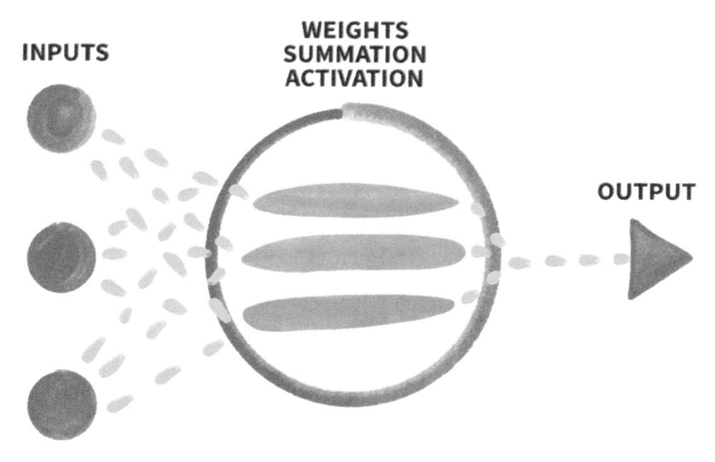

Figure 4.5. A simple feedforward neural network

This particular example of a feedforward network has a layer of inputs (not neurons), shown on the left of the diagram; a "hidden layer" of three neurons (sometimes called "nodes" or "units"), shown in the middle; and an output layer of one neuron shown on the right. Neural networks can have different numbers of inputs in the input layer, different numbers of hidden layers, and also different numbers of neurons in each of the hidden layers and the output layer.

These characteristics are all examples of **hyperparameters**, aspects of each individual neural network that the humans creating it determine before the training process begins. These settings stay constant throughout the training process. Tuning the hyperparameters of today's state-of-the-art neural networks is somewhat of an art form as opposed to a science, and the relatively small number of people in the world who are really good at it are in very high demand.

In order to understand what the neural network is capable of doing, we need to start with the inputs in the input layer. What, exactly, are they? Well, they're the **features** of whatever data is being learned by the network: individual pixels of photographs, words of text documents, short sound bites of larger audio files, or stock prices contained in spreadsheets, to name just a few possibilities. In Rosenblatt's early perceptron demonstration, the inputs to his single-neuron network were the readings of photocells and sensors that measured different aspects of the punch cards that he fed into the mainframe. Note that input nodes are not neurons. They don't do any computation at all; they just transmit the features to the neurons, or nodes, in the first hidden layer. This is why we've given them a different shape in the diagram than the neurons themselves.

Also notice that each input node in the diagram is connected to each neuron in the hidden layer. This is fairly common practice, though there are certain types of neural networks that we'll consider later that have sparse connections instead of full connections. Remember that each of these connections has its own weight, and these weights – the **parameters** of the model – get adjusted during training so that the neural network can perform its task accurately.

Deep Neural Networks

Now that we have a basic understanding of what a neural network is, what is it that makes a deep neural network "deep?" Simply, it's the number of **hidden layers** contained in the network. A hidden layer in a neural network is any layer that's in between the input layer and the output layer of the network. Any neural network that contains two or more hidden layers is considered a **deep neural network**. Unsurprisingly, then, a neural network with a single hidden layer is sometimes referred to as a **shallow neural network**.

Furthermore, the number of hidden layers corresponds to the **depth** of the deep neural network. A DNN with a depth of two would have two hidden layers, an example of which is shown in Figure 4.6. Note that the input layer (which does not contain any neurons) as well as the output layer of output neurons do not count as hidden layers. But just what do these additional hidden layers give us, anyway? Well, it turns out that they enable neural networks to learn much more intricate and abstract patterns in data than just a single layer can learn. And it's these more complex relationships in data that are often the key to tasks that typically require human intelligence. In other words, the extra hidden layers help us realize part of the promise of AI.

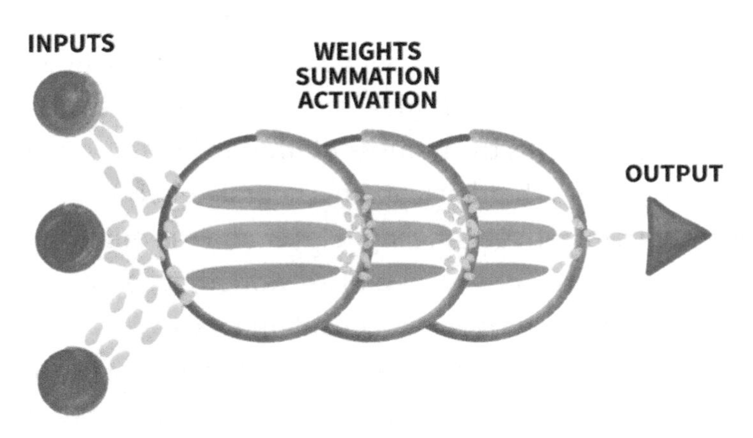

Figure 4.6. A diagram of a simple deep neural network (DNN) with a depth of two

When the pioneers of AI were first studying neural networks during the Golden Age of AI, the first two decades after the Dartmouth workshop, no one knew how to adjust the weights of the neurons in the hidden layers to improve the accuracy of the neural network's output. On top of that, experts like Marvin Minsky and Seymour Papert doubted that solving this challenge would lead to any dramatic improvements in capabilities, anyway. This skepticism steered funding and research away from neural networks in the early years.

Why was it such a challenge to figure out how to adjust the weights of the hidden neurons? Well, if you consider Rosenblatt's perceptron again, you'll notice that this single-neuron model has no hidden layers at all. In fact, it has only one single output neuron. It's very straightforward to figure out how to adjust the weights of that one output neuron to improve the accuracy of the model. Even if you add more neurons to the output layer, the problem is still relatively straightforward to solve, mathematically. You just compare the actual output with the expected (correct) output, and then you adjust the weights in the direction that reduces the difference between them.

But what do you do if the input gets fed through multiple layers of neurons? How do you know which of all the cascading weights contributed the most to the error in the output? How do you adjust these weights to reduce the overall error of the model? And what, exactly, would be the point of doing this in the first place? Back then, they didn't know the answer to any of these questions.

The challenge of figuring out how much each of the weights contributed to the error is called the **credit assignment problem**. Since it's all about determining which weights contribute the most to the error of the model, some have pointed out that a better name for it would be the "blame assignment problem." Credit or blame, the problem is the same: how much should the weights of a deep neural network be adjusted during training in order to improve the accuracy of the model's prediction?

Training Deep Neural Networks

The solution to the credit assignment problem for deep neural networks was hiding in plain sight all along, even during Frank Rosenblatt's day. A mathematical approach that had already been applied in the 1960s to optimizing rocket flight and chemical processes needed to find its way into the field of AI, which it eventually did.

The two elements of the method we now use to adjust the weights of a deep neural network during training are called **backpropagation** and **gradient descent**, and they work hand in hand. And while this approach was always theoretically valid, it wasn't until computational power and training dataset sizes increased that its potential to unlock breakthrough capabilities in neural networks became apparent. I'll describe the basic concepts of these approaches here, even if the mathematical formulas themselves go beyond the scope of this book.

Backpropagation

Backpropagation is a method that was first formalized in 1970 by Finnish mathematician and computer scientist Seppo Linnainmaa, the year before Rosenblatt's tragic boating accident. Linnainmaa's master's thesis spelled out, in plain Finnish, the steps that would eventually be applied to the adjusting of weights of hidden neurons. He didn't, however, refer to neural networks in his thesis itself. That connection was made in 1974 by American computer scientist Paul Werbos, and popularized in 1986 by David Rumelhart, Geoffrey Hinton, and Ronald Williams in their seminal paper, "Learning representations by back-propagating errors."[55]

At a conceptual level, the way backpropagation works is this. First, in what's called the **forward pass**, a training input is provided to a neural network, and the randomly generated weights of the untrained model result in activations in each neuron that flow through the network, neuron by neuron, and layer by layer, until the neurons in the output layer provide their outputs – the prediction of the model.

55. Rumelhart, D., Hinton, G., and Williams, R. Learning representations by back-propagating errors. *Nature* 323 (1986): 533–536. https://doi.org/10.1038/323533a0

Next, the **backward pass** begins. First the algorithm applies a **loss function** to calculate the error for each of the output neurons by comparing its actual output to the expected (or target) output: by how much was the prediction off? This requires knowing what the output should be – the correct prediction – for a given input. What this means, of course, is that the backpropagation algorithm is part of a supervised learning process, with training data that humans have labeled with correct outputs. Note that the term "loss function" is sometimes used interchangeably with the term **cost function**. While both of these terms do describe the error of the model, the loss function technically refers to the error in one single training example, and the cost function refers to the average error across the entire training set.

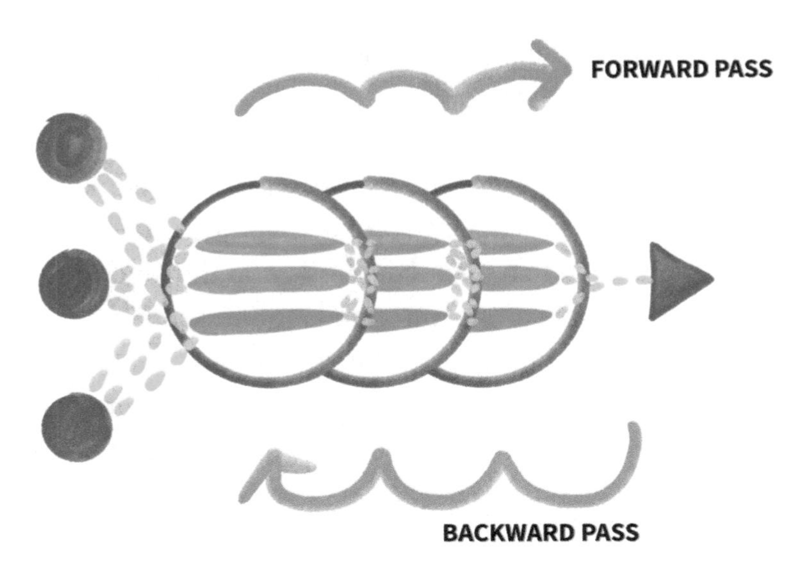

Figure 4.7. A conceptual diagram of the forward and backward pass in backpropagation

After finding the loss function of the output neurons, the algorithm does what its name suggests: it *propagates* these errors *back* through the network, layer by layer, neuron by neuron, and assigns a level of responsibility (or blame) to each individual weight of the network for the overall error of the network. This is what I referred to before as credit assignment, and it allows the algorithm to determine how much to change each weight in order to reduce the loss function and thereby improve the accuracy of output prediction.

The model doesn't just figure it all out in one single forward pass and backward pass of one training example. Rather, it goes through this process with many different training examples, over multiple iterations, each time making adjustments to the weights until it gradually reduces the error of the model. This is how a modern neural network uses training data, along with the backpropagation algorithm, to learn how to complete a task based on the patterns in the data itself, rather than based on explicit instructions on how to do the task.

Gradient Descent

The backpropagation algorithm makes use of an important mathematical technique called **gradient descent** to figure out how to modify each weight during each round of training. There are different forms of gradient descent, but the basic idea is that the algorithm finds the direction and amount of change of each weight that would reduce the model's error, or loss function, the most. The model also incorporates another hyperparameter called the **learning rate** that affects how much the weights change in each iteration. The overall algorithm is trying to reduce the error in the loss function as much as it can, and as fast as it can. In mathematical terms, it's looking for a local minimum in the loss function curve.

You can relate the process to a skier trying to get to the bottom of the ski slope to visit the lodge. The higher the skier is on the mountain, the greater the cost function of the model: lower is better. The gradient descent is analogous to the direction the skier takes: steeper is better. The learning rate is analogous to how fast the skier is going: faster isn't necessarily better. Sure, if our skier skis too slowly, it'll take a long time for her to get to the bottom. But if she skis too fast, she might blow right past the ski lodge and back up the mountain on the other side of it. Overall, the skier wants to get down the mountain to the ski lodge as fast as she can, without overshooting. To do this, she goes as fast as she thinks is prudent, while continuing to head in the direction of the steepest slope. Hopefully she's an expert skier!

Figure 4.8. Gradient descent as a skier trying to get to the lodge at the slope's bottom

As an aside, the reliance on the *slope* of the functions in backpropagation is one reason why modern neural networks use smoother, more continuous activation functions like rectified linear unit (ReLU), tanh, or sigmoid, as opposed to the threshold activation function Rosenblatt used in his perceptron. The threshold activation function has sharp edges, as shown in Figure 4.9a, jumping from a value of $y=0$ to a value of $y=1$ at the threshold value of $x=0$. If you remember from calculus class in high school, you can't find the derivative, or the slope of the curve, at an edge (or discontinuity) like this. In addition, the nonlinearity of the sigmoid and tanh functions helps the neural network find more complex relationships between inputs and outputs in the data.

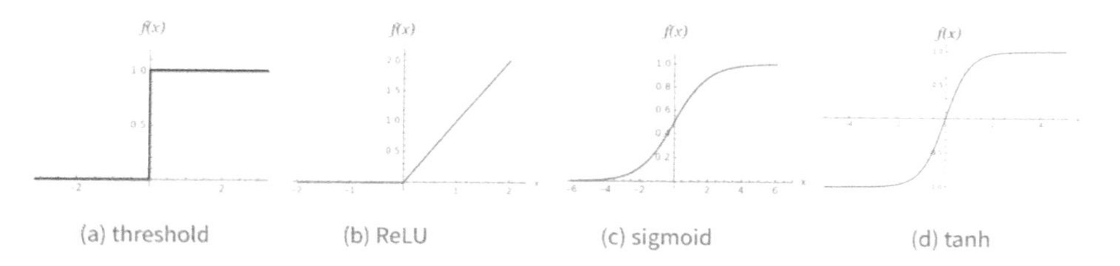

(a) threshold (b) ReLU (c) sigmoid (d) tanh

Figure 4.9. Different activation functions used in neural networks

The ability to find more complex patterns in vast data sets turns out to be the very reason that deep neural networks are so incredibly valuable. It's why they can do amazing things once thought impossible, and it's why they have become the quintessential type of artificial intelligence in our day and age. Sure, it took increases in computational power and available training data to bring about the necessary conditions for their emergence. But it also took hard work and ingenuity by talented researchers and computer scientists to develop and apply techniques like backpropagation and gradient descent, and to play with and refine different activation functions, network configurations, and hyperparameters to make deep neural networks actually work.

Types of Deep Neural Networks

Okay, that's a fair amount of technical information, even if we didn't immerse, enmesh, or ensnare ourselves in the mathematical equations behind neural networks. If you are interested in the mathematics behind the inner workings of neural networks, though, I will refer you to the free online textbook "Neural Networks and Deep Learning" by Michael Nielsen.[56]

To wrap up our own study of deep learning and neural networks, I'd like to instead consider a few different types of deep neural networks that have led to breakthrough capabilities in the fields of computer vision and natural language processing.

Convolutional Neural Networks (CNN)

The first type is the **convolutional neural network (CNN)**, sometimes called the ConvNet. This type of deep

56. Nielsen, Michael A. "Neural Networks and Deep Learning," Determination Press, 2015, http://neuralnetworksanddeeplearning.com/

neural network has produced significant breakthroughs in computer vision – giving AI models the ability to recognize objects and to analyze photographs and videos. CNNs are the reason that you and I can deposit a handwritten check into our bank account with a photograph we take using our smartphone, and they're central to advances in self-driving cars, medical imaging, and many other applications.

What's so special about CNNs and where did they come from? CNNs are based on insights about the way the human brain processes visual information. In the 1950s and 1960s, neurophysiologists David H. Hubel and Torsten N. Wiesel discovered that the visual cortex of the human brain is organized into a hierarchy of layers of neurons that are responsible for detecting increasingly complex and abstract features.

To be clearer, early layers are sensitive to simple features like lines or edges. Subsequent layers take the information from these early layers and use it to detect more complex features like corners or angles. Later layers, in turn, detect shapes like triangles or squares and pass this information downstream, where the next layers detect even more complex features like eyes or noses, then even entire faces, and so on. The layers of the CNN are designed to process images in a hierarchical way, too, hidden layer by hidden layer. A simplified version of this hierarchy is shown in Figure 4.10.

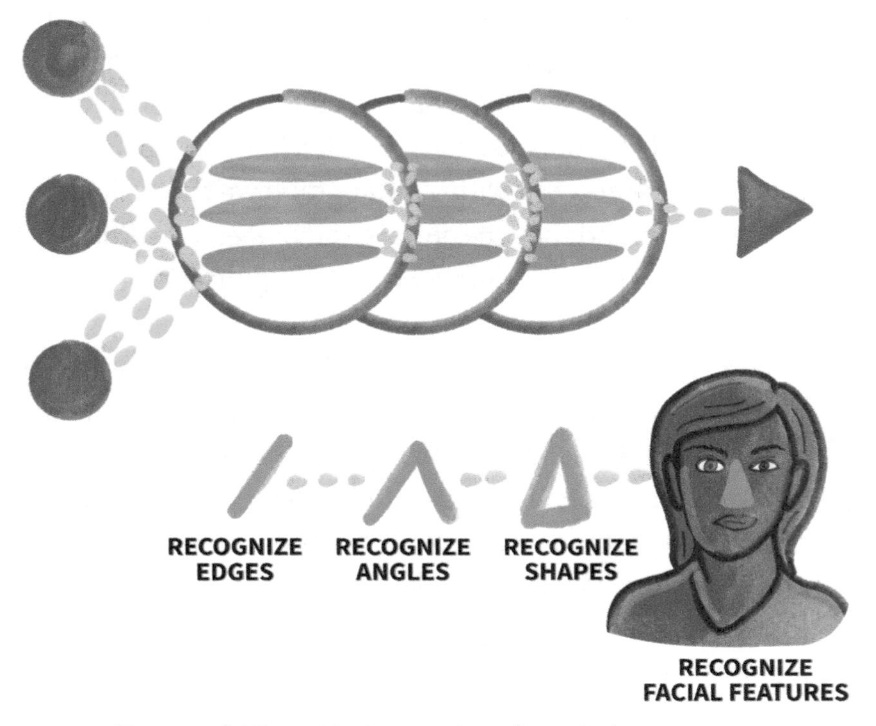

Figure 4.10. Hierarchical processing of visual information

The development of CNNs by Yann LeCun in the 1980s was inspired by this hierarchical processing of visual information, as was its predecessor, Kunihiko Fukushima's neocognitron in the 1970s. In 1979, Fukushima trained his neocognitron to recognize handwritten Japanese characters, and in 1989, LeCun used a version of the CNN that employed backpropagation and gradient descent to recognize handwritten zip codes with a degree of accuracy never seen before.

So how does a CNN work? While there are other applications, most commonly the inputs to a CNN are the RGB (red-green-blue) values of the pixels in an image or video. Instead of connecting each and every pixel to each and every neuron in the first hidden layer, the CNN instead applies a series of filters that are designed to detect specific types of features in the image. A **filter**, also known as a **kernel**, is an array of weights designed to detect certain features in the image. One filter, for example, might detect horizontal edges, while another detects vertical edges.

A filter doesn't examine the entire image at once. Instead, it applies to a small portion or patch of the image, for example, a 3x3 grid of 9 pixels, that gradually slides and snakes its way across the image (hence the term "convolution," which means a coil or a twist) until a **feature map** has been created that highlights where that filter finds its specific feature in the image. Each filter makes its own feature map indicating where its corresponding feature is located in the image. For a conceptual representation of how this convolution process works for a given filter, see the way the 3x3 grid moves across the image in Figure 4.11.

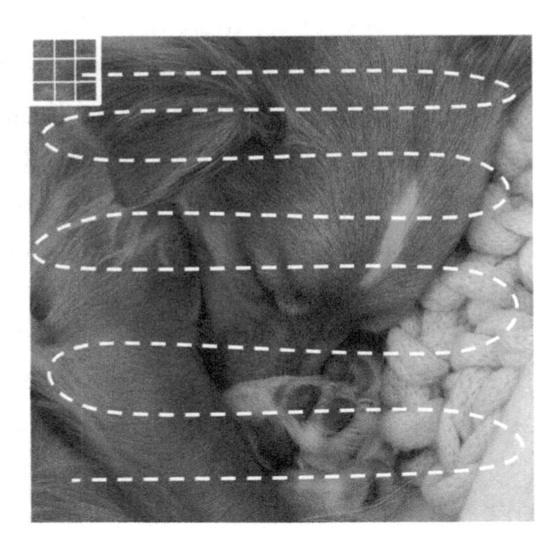

Figure 4.11. A conceptual image of a 3x3 filter grid (not shown to size) and its convolutional path across the image

Each neuron in the convolutional layers is associated with one position of a specific filter as it makes its way around the image. The weights applied to each neuron in a convolutional layer are all the same, enabling the layer to find the specific feature that the filter is looking for, say a dog's paw, no matter where it's located in the image. If the dog's paw is in the top left corner of the image, then the neuron focusing on that specific location will find it. If the dog's paw is in the center of the image, then another neuron will find it – the one associated with the same filter in the centered location – because these neurons have the same exact weights.

The CNN also applies activation functions (typically ReLU) to these convolutional neurons to introduce nonlinearity to the network so that it can find more complex patterns and apply gradient descent during training. It also includes additional layers after the convolutional layers, such as pooling layers that reduce the dimensionality of each feature map, and classification layers that output an object or list of objects found in the image.

A CNN is trained on a large set of labeled images, and the backpropagation and gradient descent techniques are applied to adjust the individual weights of each filter so that the CNN can learn how to detect meaningful features in the training images. This, of course, allows it to do what we want to use it for: namely, to analyze new images not included in the training set.

Generative Adversarial Networks (GAN)

Generative adversarial networks (GANs), introduced by Ian Goodfellow and his colleagues in 2014, consist of pairs of neural networks coupled together in training. One of the two models in the pair is the **generator**, which tries to generate an output (it could be words, images, audio, or video) that's indistinguishable from real data. Think of an image of a face that looks so real that you can't tell it doesn't actually belong to a real person.

The other neural network in the pair is the **discriminator**. Its job is to determine whether a given input is a real sample from its training data, or a fake that has been created by the generator. These two neural networks are trained together and compete against one another, and are therefore in an "adversarial" relationship.

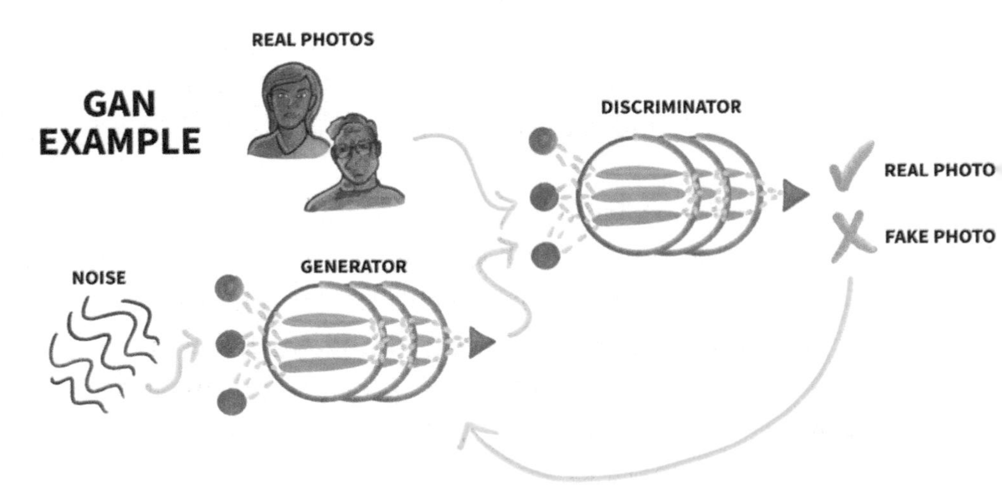

Figure 4.12. A conceptual diagram of a generative adversarial network (GAN)

At first, the generator creates a fake based on random noise. As you can imagine, it's not difficult at the beginning for the discriminator to figure out when it has been presented with a fake from the generator as opposed to a real image from the sample set.

However, the results of each training round are fed back into the generator in an iterative way. Over the course of many rounds of training, the generator learns how to make fakes that are more and more like the real thing. The discriminator, at the same time, learns to pick up on more and more subtle clues that give away the fake. The process forms a continuous improvement loop for both the generator and the discriminator.

The goal of the process is typically to train the generator to create fake content that's so hard to distinguish from the real thing that the discriminator doesn't have anything better than a 50/50 chance at getting it right. We'll consider some of the ethical problems associated with generative AI models that can create hyper-realistic content, such as deepfakes that are misleading or harmful in various ways.

The Transformer and Large Language Models (LLMs)

A large language model (LLM) is a particular type of deep neural network that has been trained on massive amounts of text data to process and generate human language. State-of-the-art LLMs have billions of parameters – the weights and biases of its many neurons – that have been adjusted and fine-tuned during training to enable these models to produce outputs that resemble human speech.

Today's advanced LLMs, such as OpenAI's GPT-4, Meta's LLaMA 2, and Mistral AI's Mixtral-8x7B, can perform a wide array of human language tasks with speed and relatively high accuracy. Due to their limitations as well as the many imperfections and biases inherent in their training data, they're by no means perfect. But there's no denying that they're incredibly capable and powerful. One reason for their recent surge in capabilities is the pivot to a technology known as the transformer.

The transformer architecture was first introduced by Google researchers in their 2017 paper "Attention Is All You Need."[57] A **transformer** is a specific type of neural network that uses an advancement called the **self-attention mechanism** that enables the model to consider every single **token** (words, fragments of words, or even individual letters) in an entire sequence at the same time, rather than just one token at a time. Additionally, the transformer uses feedforward neural networks to process the output of the self-attention mechanisms. Transformers have largely replaced recurrent neural networks (RNNs) and long short-term memory (LSTM) networks in many NLP tasks due to their superior performance.

In effect, what the transformer does is that it assigns a score to each token in the sequence according to its importance in predicting the next token. Take the phrase "more than meets the..." What word comes next? We know that the next word is likely to be "eye." From messaging platforms to text editors, software that we use every single day has been predicting the next word for us for years now. The Google Docs file I am typing in right now attempts to fill in the gaps as I type this very sentence.

Transformers are more than mere "next word predictors," though. Their ability to process all words at once, along with their massive amount of training data, enable them to perform much more complex natural language tasks. The

57. Vaswani, A., Shazeer, N. Parmar, N., Uszkoreit, J., Jones, L., Gomez, A. N., Kaiser, L., and Polosukhin, I., "Attention Is All You Need," *Advances in Neural Information Processing Systems* 30 (June 12, 2017), arXiv.Org. https://arxiv.org/abs/1706.03762

attention mechanism is what allows the model to focus on different parts of the input sequence when generating a response to a prompt. This gives the model an ability to work with context and relationships between words. Transformers are being applied to other domains as well, not just language processing, including computer vision and audio processing.

In November 2022, OpenAI released ChatGPT to the public. At launch, ChatGPT used their GPT-3.5 large language model, an improvement over their GPT-3 model, whose 175 billion parameters had been trained on 570GB of text obtained from internet sites like Wikipedia as well as books, research articles, and other text sources. The acronym "GPT" in ChatGPT stands for **generative pre-trained transformer.**" OpenAI has since released the GPT-4 model, though they are no longer sharing openly the number of parameters of the model nor the size of its training data due to the increasingly competitive nature of the space.

OpenAI's approach has been to "pre-train" their models on billions of sentences to predict what comes next. Then they fine-tune the pre-trained model by having human reviewers read and rate various outputs of the models. This process is called **reinforcement learning from human feedback (RLHF)**.[58] As OpenAI themselves admit, the result of this process is far from perfect. In effect, the model is learning to provide outputs that the human trainers like and prefer. You can imagine that there would be both benefits as well

58. "Introducing ChatGPT." OpenAI, November 30, 2022, https://openai.com/blog/chatgpt

as drawbacks associated with training AI to tell us what we want to hear.

Summary

There's no denying that deep learning has revolutionized AI technology in general, and our world as a whole. Now you have a better understanding of what it is, where it came from, how it fits into the overall AI picture, and why it has been so powerful and transformational. Deep learning has thrived in the era of Big Data. Deep neural networks are trained on massive data sets using cutting-edge computational processes and hardware such as GPUs that are able to perform the large number of calculations necessary in a relatively short amount of time.

Neural networks and deep learning were born out of inspiration drawn from the way the human brain works. The way they actually function, of course, is quite different from the way biological brains function, but the roots are evident in a basic comparison of an artificial neuron and a biological neuron. The simplest form of neural network, Frank Rosenblatt's single-neuron device called the perceptron, was around in the earliest days of the field of AI, but interest and funding dwindled due to difficulties training networks with multiple hidden layers, or deep neural networks.

In spite of the lack of enthusiasm for neural networks during the 1970s and 1980s, research continued in the background among a relatively small number of dedicated experts. Over time, a series of breakthroughs in the training of deep neural networks—specifically the application of backpropagation, gradient descent, and activation functions like ReLU, sigmoid, and tanh—led to advances that could no longer be ignored.

A series of innovative neural network architectures have led to huge leaps in capabilities in computer vision (convolutional neural networks, CNNs), image generation (generative adversarial networks, GANs), and natural language processing (transformers). Because of these evolutionary bursts, the pendulum of interest has swung toward subsymbolic, or connectionist, AI, where it remains to this day.

Where will it go from here? I, for one, believe that more advances are needed in symbolic AI in order to bolster the reliability of deep neural networks, which tend to confabulate, or hallucinate, and create nonsensical outputs. There's no reason that symbolic AI and subsymbolic AI need to be mutually exclusive. It reminds me of the old beer commercial I saw on television a while back, where one group of bar patrons yells that a particular beer "tastes great," while another yells back that it's "less filling." The point of the commercial, of course, is that the beer is great for both reasons, and there's no need to argue. In like manner, AI can be great if it's able to both learn from data (subsymbolic AI) and have rules-based knowledge about the world (symbolic AI).

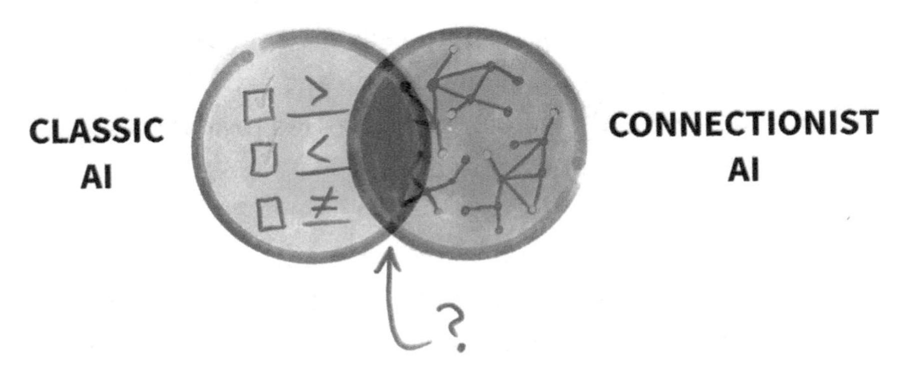

Figure 4.13. Perhaps the overlap of classic AI and connectionist AI will unlock yet another evolutionary leap in AI

PART 3

Important Considerations in AI

CHAPTER 5

AI Benefits and Concerns

"AI is a tool.
The choice about how it gets deployed is ours."
– Oren Etzioni

At this point in our journey into the world of AI, we need to consider its impact on the real world. We cannot come to fully understand a technology without considering its impact on our planet and life on it, particularly human life.

Can you imagine trying to tell the story of the automobile in the 20th century without mentioning its impact on society, the economy, and the environment? We can study the inner workings of the internal combustion engine, and we can compare different kinds of automobiles, from cars to minivans to trucks and SUVs. But we won't truly understand the automobile until we examine the effect on everyday life, the transformation of modern cities and suburbs, and the impact on carbon dioxide emissions, among other important factors. These factors are not footnotes in the story of the automobile; they *are* the story.

Up until this point in the book, we've considered a number of aspects of AI, from various definitions and the main types and branches, to the history of the field, to the different approaches and methods that have propelled the technology forward to where it is today. We've laid a solid foundation of understanding about machine learning and deep learning. But we haven't yet stopped to consider how AI has changed us. Let's pivot, then, from the technical to the personal.

It would be very easy to take a one-sided perspective in this discussion. Certainly many people do. At one extreme, you'll find AI enthusiasts and technophiles who trumpet the virtues of AI. This revolutionary technology, they say, will usher in a paradise of prosperity for all. These "AI homers" often stand to make a lot of money if adoption of the technology continues accelerating. At the other extreme, you'll find "AI haters" and technophobes who bang the drum of doom and gloom about how AI will ruin our livelihoods and our very lives. They warn of the coming dystopia of subservience to the robots.

This is nothing new. Other major technological breakthroughs in human history have produced a similar polarization of responses. In 19th-century England, a band of craftsmen called the Luddites rioted and destroyed textile machinery that was displacing their labor. Protests, worker strikes, and vocal opposition have arisen to other, more recent technological innovations, too, such as nuclear power, genetically modified organisms (GMOs), and autonomous vehicles, to name a few. It seems that part of the human psyche is hardwired to be hopeful about technological change and the other part is hardwired to be fearful about it.

In this chapter, I'm going to present what I feel is a balanced perspective about the benefits and harms of AI. To be honest, the voice of the inner optimist and the voice of the inner pessimist both swirl around in my head relative to this transformational set of technologies. I'm excited about some of the transformations that AI is bringing, but I'm also apprehensive about others that come with them. I tend to agree with American author, educator, and cultural critic Neil Postman about the double-edged nature of the sword of technology:

"It is a mistake to suppose that any technological innovation has a one-sided effect.
Every technology is both a burden and a blessing; not either-or, but this-and-that."[59]

In order to investigate both the blessings as well as the burdens of AI, we'll step through a series of categories in this chapter, and we'll try to look at the situation through both lenses. Let's start with the way we get work done, the very topic about which AI makes the most direct claims.

59. Postman, Neil, *Technopoly: The Surrender of Culture to Technology* (New York: Knopf, 1992).

Automation and Decision-Making

Benefits in the Workplace

A central promise of AI is that it will free us from tedious, repetitive, boring work. Let's examine that claim. On the one hand, we can certainly make the case that it is delivering on that promise. AI is currently being used to automate business processes and household chores alike. There are far too many examples of this to list them all, but I'll name a few for posterity.

Document processing tools like Amazon Textract or Azure AI Document Intelligence from Microsoft use machine learning to extract text, handwriting, layout elements, and data from scanned documents such as loan applications or purchase receipts, saving companies countless hours of manual data entry and enabling them to process documents much faster and more accurately than any human could ever do.

AI is also being used in the legal profession to review contracts, laws, or historical cases to find unusual clauses or sections of noncompliance in a fraction of the time it used to take. Instead of tasking a junior attorney with pouring over thousands of pages of documents, AI tools that use natural language processing (NLP) can search, tag, categorize, summarize, and analyze the same amount of text in a fraction of the time.

In my own business, we use large language models to help us identify key themes in responses to open-ended survey questions that used to take us hours to comb through and manually categorize. What used to amount to tiring mental labor now takes a few clicks and less than a minute to complete.

This is just a handful of examples of how AI is assisting in the carrying out of what once were menial tasks in the workplace. It wouldn't be overstating it to say that every department in every industry now uses AI to save human workers from tedium, often without the workers even knowing it. Many of these AI systems don't just complete boring tasks – though, they also make automated decisions based on data.

In my previous writings, I have stated my preference for the term "data-informed" rather than "data-driven" in contexts involving a "human-in-the-loop" (HITL) of the decision-making process. When a human is in the loop, data is a useful input, but it should not be what actually drives the decision. The human and their goals and values should be what drive the decision.

When the reins of a process have been entirely turned over to AI, however, the decision truly is a data-driven one. As a case in point, technology workers at Amazon may review the performance of a product recommendation engine, but no one sits there and chooses, customer by customer, pageview by pageview, what products to suggest based on data inputs. It would require a massive staff of data analysts and marketers to deliver such personalization.

Businesses are using AI to automate decisions about inventory management in operations, online advertising in marketing, lead scoring in sales, fraud detection in finance, resume screening in human resources, predictive maintenance in manufacturing – the list goes on and on. AI is already a workhorse in the workplace.

Benefits in the Home

The workplace isn't the only place where humans are being spared the burden of carrying out mind- and finger-numbing tasks. In the home, AI is taking over many of the chores that humans used to have to do themselves. Newer versions of the Roomba robot vacuum cleaner by iRobot, for example, use machine learning to create a map of a house, adapt to changes in the home, and identify and avoid objects in the room like furniture or, critically, dog poop on the floor. Just hope that it doesn't automatically take a photo of you while you're on the toilet!

Now, automation is nothing new, nor is it necessarily dependent on AI. Just think of the traditional dishwasher, whose machinery, sensors, timers, and software have allowed it to offload a chore considered by many (especially teenagers) to be odious. The traditional dishwasher – the one from my childhood – did not use AI. Newer AI-powered robots are being developed, however, such as the Spotless by a company called Nala Robotics, that use "high-performance camera systems and machine learning" to fully automate the dishwashing process, from picking up bowls to the dumping of scraps in the garbage to washing and placing in the drying rack.[60] Where were they when I was a kid?

Other examples of AI-powered automation and data-driven decision-making in the home aren't so futuristic. Heating, ventilation, and air conditioning (HVAC) systems already use machine learning to process data from temperature and humidity sensors to optimize the system in various ways, driving efficiencies that can reduce energy bills for homeowners without their involvement or even their awareness in the process. This is just one of the many "smart home" systems that automate tasks around the house, increase efficiencies, alert us about problems, and even schedule preventative maintenance for us.

The Burden of Ease

This might sound like a crazy question, but what price do we pay to offload these time-consuming, labor-intensive tasks to AI? Is there a downside to being relieved of the need to make tedious, repetitive decisions ourselves? On the surface, these would seem to be blessings without any burden whatsoever. And my 15-year-old self would probably have argued vehemently that a fully automated

60. "Spotless Fully Automated Robotic Dishwasher," Nala Robotics, https://nalarobotics.com/spotless.html, Last accessed on February 25, 2024

dishwashing robot would be the equivalent of a rose without a single thorn. I loathed that chore.

Are all of these manual tasks really so bad, though? Do we, in fact, lose something by giving up the privilege of doing them ourselves? I can see my teenage self's eyes rolling all the way back into his head at the argument my 45-year-old self is about to make, but I submit to you, dear reader, that you and I can build character and learn how to connect with ourselves and our world by engaging in the everyday chore, as menial as it may seem. This quote from the late Vietnamese Buddhist monk Thich Nhat Hanh expresses the point eloquently:

"While washing the dishes one should only be washing the dishes, which means that while washing the dishes one should be completely aware of the fact that one is washing the dishes....
The fact that I am standing there and washing these bowls is a wondrous reality. I'm being completely myself, following my breath, conscious of my presence, and conscious of my thoughts and actions. There's no way I can be tossed around mindlessly like a bottle slapped here and there on the waves."[61]

61. Nhất Hạnh, Thích, *The Miracle of Mindfulness: A Manual on Meditation* (Boston: Beacon Press, 1987).

Doing the dishes can actually be seen as an opportunity to grasp rather than a burden to cast off. Earlier this week, we had a wonderful dinner party at our home in Palm Springs, California, complete with home-cooked vegetable soup made by my wife, Becky, who makes delicious meals. As the hours of enjoyment went by, I found myself needing a break from the commotion, a quiet moment to myself. My refuge? The stack of dirty dishes in the kitchen. After a good 10 or 15 minutes of washing and breathing and hearing the chatter continue across the room, I was ready to reengage with our guests.

That's fine for household chores, but what about in the office? Surely a new-age, quasi-spiritual argument for the value of manual labor doesn't apply. Well, do you know what happened with that AI-powered survey analysis tool we implemented at Data Literacy, the one that automatically summarizes open-ended responses for us? In the end, I went back to reading each customer's response myself, one by one.

Don't get me wrong, I still use the amazing text summarization capabilities of the large language model we have tailored to the task. But I feel connected to the feedback in a deeper way when I read the words that our customers themselves have typed out. There is valuable nuance in the details that I don't want to lose. I actually use the LLM as I read through each response and I compare how AI would categorize the feedback to how I would categorize it. In doing so, I learn not only about my customers, but about how the AI works too, both its capabilities and its quirks.

I do not mean to say, by the way, that we should never turn over a task to AI, or to any other form of technology. I simply mean to say that we should consider what we lose by giving it up. And furthermore, we should consider, before fully abdicating our control, whether there is a middle ground in which we can partner with AI to get the job done together. In some cases, taking the middle path of HITL will keep us connected to the details of the work while also saving us a significant amount of time and energy – the best of both worlds.

The So-Called Existential Threat

While we're on the topic of AI automatically doing tasks and making decisions for us, it seems like a good time to mention a controversial concern that some people have, and others like to mock: the **existential threat** to the human species that AI allegedly poses. I say "allegedly poses" because the existential threat is hypothetical, strictly speaking. There's a good chance (though impossible to quantify) that it will never actually happen.

Let's hope it doesn't, because the concern goes like this: AI continues getting smarter and smarter at some exponential rate until it becomes as intelligent as human beings. That would be the point at which artificial general intelligence (AGI) becomes a reality. So far so good.

The fear, though, is that AI won't stop there. What if AI continues getting smarter than us? Perhaps at some point, called the **technological singularity**, AI will enter a continuous and uncontrollable loop of self-improvement that results in an explosion of intelligence that dwarfs our own, or so the thinking goes. Many brilliant people are terrified of this possibility. In a 2014 interview with the BBC, the late English physicist Stephen Hawking famously warned:

> **"The development of full artificial intelligence could spell the end of the human race....It would take off on its own, and re-design itself at an ever increasing rate. Humans, who are limited by slow biological evolution, couldn't compete, and would be superseded."**[62]

In his 2005 book *The Singularity is Near: When Humans Transcend Biology*, futurist and AI optimist Ray Kurzweil, an American computer scientist and author, predicted that the singularity would happen four decades after the time he wrote the book:

> **"I set the date for the Singularity – representing a profound and disruptive transformation in human capability – as 2045. The nonbiological intelligence**

62. Cellan-Jones, Rory. "Stephen Hawking Warns Artificial Intelligence Could End Mankind." BBC. December 2, 2014. https://www.bbc.com/news/technology-30290540

created in that year will be one billion times more powerful than all human intelligence today."[63]

Now, while it's true that the capabilities of AI have been increasing at an incredible rate over the past few decades, exponentially growing phenomena are notoriously difficult to forecast. There's certainly no guarantee that the intelligence of computers will continue to expand at an exponential rate indefinitely. Besides, even if AI becomes more intelligent than humans, it's not a foregone conclusion that it will want to destroy us or subjugate us.

There are those who point out that, however unlikely, this possibility still exists. They include Turing Award winner Geoffrey Hinton, pioneer of deep learning and backpropagation, who quit his job at Google in April 2023 to speak out more freely about the risks of the technologies he helped to bring about. Experts like Hinton tend to emphasize the importance of solving the **alignment problem**, which is primarily concerned with making sure that the goals of any AI system are aligned with the goals and preferences of humans. Hinton and others seek to prevent the development of a superintelligent AI that is misaligned with the goals of humans, and therefore a danger to our civilization. Here is how Hinton himself described the challenge:

63. Kurzweil, Ray, *The Singularity Is Near: When Humans Transcend Biology* (New York: Viking, 2005).

"What we want is some way of making sure that even if they're smarter than us, they're going to do things that are beneficial for us."[64]

I vacillate in my concern about the existential threat posed by AI. There are times when I do worry about it, and other times when it all seems like science fiction. I believe it makes sense that smart people continue to work on the alignment problem. My current level of concern is not high enough that I feel compelled to throw myself into such an endeavor. My opinion is that there are more immediate concerns related to real and present dangers posed by AI that we'll consider next.

Economic and Financial

Economic and Financial Benefits

A growing body of research findings lends credence to the belief that AI is reducing tedious manual labor in the workplace and freeing up knowledge workers to tackle more advanced tasks. These productivity gains are adding to the bottom line of companies and to the economic output of countries that are embracing AI. On top of productivity gains, in a somewhat self-fulfilling prophecy, new AI models and systems are giving technology companies plenty of additional opportunities to make even

64. Brown, Sara. "Why Neural Net Pioneer Geoffrey Hinton Is Sounding the Alarm on AI." MIT Sloan School of Management. May 23, 2023. Last accessed February 25, 2024, https://mitsloan.mit.edu/ideas-made-to-matter/why-neural-net-pioneer-geoffrey-hinton-sounding-alarm-ai

more of a profit by releasing new AI-based products and by enhancing existing products with new AI functionalities.

According to a 2023 research report by Goldman Sachs economists Joseph Briggs and Devesh Kodnani, generative AI could contribute significantly to the global economy in the decade following the publication of the report:

> *As tools using advances in natural language processing work their way into businesses and society, they could drive a 7% (or almost $7 trillion) increase in global GDP and lift productivity growth by 1.5 percentage points over a 10-year period.*[65]

Who knows whether this prediction will prove to be an accurate one? It seems possible that generative AI and NLP could generate a lot more than that, and, depending on various factors that are difficult to predict (such as government regulations and pending litigation outcomes), it could also generate a lot less than that. Time will tell.

At the level of an individual worker, studies are being published that seem to show that knowledge workers who embrace generative AI can do more work in a given amount of time, and the quality and accuracy of the work they do increases as well, though that depends on how they use advanced tools, and what they try to use them for.

65. "Generative AI Could Raise Global GDP by 7%." Goldman Sachs. April 5, 2023. Last accessed February 25, 2024. https://www.goldmansachs.com/intelligence/pages/generative-ai-could-raise-global-gdp-by-7-percent.htm

For example, in their 2023 working paper *Navigating the Jagged Technological Frontier: Field Experimental Evidence of the Effects of AI on Knowledge Worker Productivity and Quality*,[66] a team of Harvard Business School researchers led by Fabrizio Dell'Acqua shared the results of an experiment they conducted with over 700 consultants at Boston Consulting Group.

They found that such highly skilled knowledge workers achieved a 12% increase in productivity, a 40% increase in quality, and a time savings of 25% on average when using generative AI tools to complete tasks that are "inside the frontier" of the capabilities of those tools, meaning tasks that are easily done by AI. On the flipside, though, when given tasks that are "outside the frontier" of these capabilities, "consultants using AI were 19 percentage points less likely to produce correct solutions compared to those without AI."

What these findings suggest, then, is that in order to reap the benefits of AI, it's critical to identify which tasks are inside the frontier of AI capabilities, and which tasks are outside of the frontier of those capabilities. Further complicating matters, this frontier is not static, it's dynamic. And it's not always clear to workers whether a specific task is inside the frontier or outside of it. Nevertheless,

66. Dell'Acqua, F., E. McFowland, E.R. Mollick, H. Lifshitz-Assaf, K. Kellogg, S. Rajendran, et al., "Navigating the Jagged Technological Frontier: Field Experimental Evidence of the Effects of AI on Knowledge Worker Productivity and Quality," Harvard Business School Technology & Operations Mgt. Unit Working Paper No. 24-013, September 2023, https://papers.ssrn.com/sol3/papers.cfm?abstract_id=4573321

the potential is there for significant gains in productivity and quality. Workers and companies that find ways to capitalize on these benefits stand to reap the reward of the advantages that AI can confer.

Job Displacement and Economic Inequality

Whenever a transformational new technology enters the marketplace, it eliminates some jobs, augments or complements other jobs, and creates some brand new jobs as well. It isn't always obvious beforehand or even in the early stages how a particular new technology will affect different jobs and different industries. And it's hard to predict what the net effect of shifts in employment levels will be. Will overall unemployment levels increase or decrease as a result of a technological innovation?

Uncertainty breeds fear, especially when the fear is a financial one. I'll never forget my 10th-grade U.S. history teacher, Don Schotliff, at Thousand Oaks High School in California standing on top of his desk, holding his wallet high up in the air, and screaming at the top of his lungs. He got the point across to a classroom full of very startled sophomores – Americans get cranky when something affects or threatens to affect their pocketbook.

It's thus understandable that the emergence of new technologies triggers fears and insecurities about job losses. An important question to ask is whether some groups are more likely to benefit from AI, and other groups are more likely to suffer because of it. As specific AI systems emerge, who gains wealth and power and who loses wealth and power as a result?

One concern that exists about AI is that it will accelerate a recent and alarming trend in the world, namely that the very rich are getting even richer and the very poor are getting even poorer. In analysis published in January 2024, International Monetary Fund (IMF) staff warned of the potential that AI could further deepen inequality within individual economies:

> *AI could also affect income and wealth inequality within countries. We may see polarization within income brackets, with workers who can harness AI seeing an increase in their productivity and wages—and those who cannot falling behind.*[67]

The IMF study further specifies which groups of workers are currently at higher risk of losing out due to AI. Their model simulations suggest that "workers without postsecondary education show reduced mobility," and "older workers may struggle with reemployment, adapting to technology, mobility, and training for new job skills." And who is most likely to come out ahead thanks to AI, according to the study? You guessed it: "AI's gains will likely disproportionately accrue to higher-income earners."

67. Cazzaniga, Mauro, et al., "Gen-AI: Artificial Intelligence and the Future of Work." International Monetary Fund, January 14, 2024, https://www.imf.org/en/Publications/Staff-Discussion-Notes/Issues/2024/01/14/Gen-AI-Artificial-Intelligence-and-the-Future-of-Work-542379?cid=bl-com-SDNEA2024001

On top of the possibility of deepening inequalities within individual economies, the IMF study further warns that the gap between wealthier countries and poorer countries could get even wider due to global shifts resulting from the AI revolution that's underway:

> *Over time, the AI divide could exacerbate existing economic disparities, with advanced economies harnessing AI for competitive advantage while emerging market and developing economies grapple with integrating AI into their growth models.*

Now, the IMF study authors acknowledge the significant uncertainties that exist at this early stage of the deep learning revolution. What will governments do to regulate AI? What will happen in ongoing legal disputes about the way these tools are being used? How will specific industries and societies react to AI, and how will social pressures affect the decisions that people make about these tools? We don't know. But we can say for certain that the potential is there for poorer, older, and less educated workers to suffer disproportionately.

Environmental and Societal

Sustainable Development Goals

In spite of these reasonable concerns about AI's effect on the distribution of wealth, it's likely that we will continue to find uses for AI that bring benefits to communities and societies, and that help us make strides relative to the 17 UN Sustainable Development Goals (SDGs). These goals include giving citizens of the world access to a quality education, clean water and sanitation, affordable and clean energy, and sustainable cities and communities, among others.

AI's current impact on the environment is a mixed bag. The GPUs and data centers involved in the training and operating of state-of-the-art deep neural networks like ChatGPT require massive amounts of energy to power and cool. This places a significant burden on the environment. On the other hand, AI is being used to better manage energy grids and efficiently distribute electricity.

AI can also optimize the performance and increase the output of alternative energy systems such as wind turbines and solar panels, figuring out where to place them and how to orient them to best capture energy from these "green" sources. And autonomous vehicles, or self-driving cars, use AI to operate electric vehicles with zero tailpipe emissions in a smoother, more eco-friendly manner, even if their batteries are sometimes manufactured using energy that comes from coal power plants.

The net effect of all of these positive and negative impacts on the environment is as hard to determine as the net effect of AI on jobs and the economy. Predicting how the net effects will change in the future is even more difficult. In the case of the environment, it's at least possible that the net effect of AI will be favorable, an outcome that's sorely needed to secure our future based on the continuous rise of mean global temperatures.

As for how AI can be used to safeguard human life, statistical models can identify and alert communities to elevated risks of natural disasters such as floods, earthquakes, tsunamis, and wildfires. According to the World Health Organization, more than 600,000 people died from malaria in 2022 alone.[68] A company called Zzapp Malaria makes software that uses AI to analyze satellite imagery and topographic maps to identify malaria transmission hotspots and for mosquito surveillance.

AI is also being used to combat hunger around the world, which is the second of the 17 SDGs: "Zero Hunger." World Food Programme (WFP), an international organization with the UN that brings life-saving food assistance to those in need around the world, tracks global hunger in near

68. World malaria report 2022. Geneva: World Health Organization; 2022. License: CC BY-NC-SA 3.0 IGO, https://www.who.int/publications/i/item/9789240064898

real-time through their HungerMap Live project.[69] The project uses "machine learning-based predictive models to estimate the food security situation" in places where the data is sparse or unavailable.

Bias and Fairness

We've been considering many different benefits and concerns of AI, some of them real and some of them hypothetical. But we have not yet addressed the elephant in the room: bias. I'm not talking about statistical bias, nor am I referring to the bias term in a neural network. I'm talking about **algorithmic bias**, which we can define as "systematic and repeatable errors in a computer system that create 'unfair' outcomes, such as 'privileging' one category over another in ways different from the intended function of the algorithm."[70] Let's unpack this.

It's critical to remember that the entire goal of machine learning and deep learning is to give computers the ability to learn from data how to perform tasks. We've learned of different ways computers can learn, from supervised learning to unsupervised learning to reinforcement learning. Regardless of the method, training requires data. And much of that data is obtained from the world in which we live: internet message boards, scraped webpages, repositories of uploaded images and videos, basically

69. World Food Programme. 'HungerMap LIVE.' Accessed February 25, 2024. https://hungermap.wfp.org/
70. Wikipedia contributors. 'Algorithmic Bias.' Wikipedia. Last modified February 25, 2024. https://en.wikipedia.org/wiki/Algorithmic_bias

anything that the companies that train these models can get their hands on.

Here's the dirty little secret, though: data is dirty. Every data set, including training data sets used in machine learning, contains deficiencies and problems of various kinds, including missing values, or nulls, typos, mixed units of measure, and missing decimal places, just to name a few. These errors and inaccuracies are quite common, and unfortunately the AI model learns from them, too. How could it not?

While it may require a lot of effort and cost, data can be cleaned, and errors can be removed or fixed. But there's a more persistent, pernicious problem with real-world data: it was collected from a real world that has real inequities and real unfairness woven into its very fabric. What do I mean, and how does this work its way into AI models that negatively affect real people? Let's consider some examples.

In my 2023 book *Leading in the Age of Data*, I shared a case study from the world of corporate recruiting that I find fascinating. In a 2018 article, Reuters reporter Jeffrey Dastin wrote about how Amazon had made the decision to scrap an AI recruiting tool that was showing bias against women.[71] A team at Amazon had been using

71. Dastin, Jeffrey, "Amazon Scraps Secret AI Recruiting Tool That Showed Bias Against Women," Reuters, October 10, 2018, https://www.reuters.com/article/us-amazon-com-jobs-automation-insight/amazon-scraps-secret-ai-recruiting-tool-that-showed-bias-against-women-idUSKCN1MK08G

machine learning to train a program to review applicants' resumés. Their goal was to use the program to analyze newly submitted resumés and assign job candidates a score ranging from one to five stars, kind of like the ratings we see on books and products that we purchase on their website. That way, hiring managers could simply sort by the top-rated candidates and hire those individuals, passing over candidates with lower ratings.

It didn't take long for them to notice, however, that the program was rating applicants for software development jobs in a gender-biased manner. Since a high percentage of software developers in the previous 10-year period had been men, the model trained itself on their resumés, resulting in poorer scores for resumés that included words more likely to be found on a female applicant's resumés. According to Dastin:

> *In effect, Amazon's system taught itself that male candidates were preferable. It penalized resumes that included the word 'women's,' as in 'women's chess club captain.' And it downgraded graduates of two all-women's colleges, according to people familiar with the matter.*

As the article mentions, Amazon decided not to use this technology, and according to the company, they actually disbanded the team that created it. Luckily, in this case, the creators of an AI caught its discriminatory behavior before it did any (or at least much) harm. In other situations, that's not the case. The current state of generative AI, for example, can result in outputs that are full of such biases.

For example, in my other 2023 book, *ChatGPT Basics*, I shared the results of the following prompt that I submitted to OpenAI's GPT-3.5 and GPT-4 via the popular ChatGPT platform on March 15, 2023: *Tell me a story of 100 words about a nurse who received an award for bravery.* I asked both GPT models this same exact question and repeated it 40 times for each model, resulting in 80 total responses. Figure 5.1 gives one of the responses the GPT-3.5 model provided.

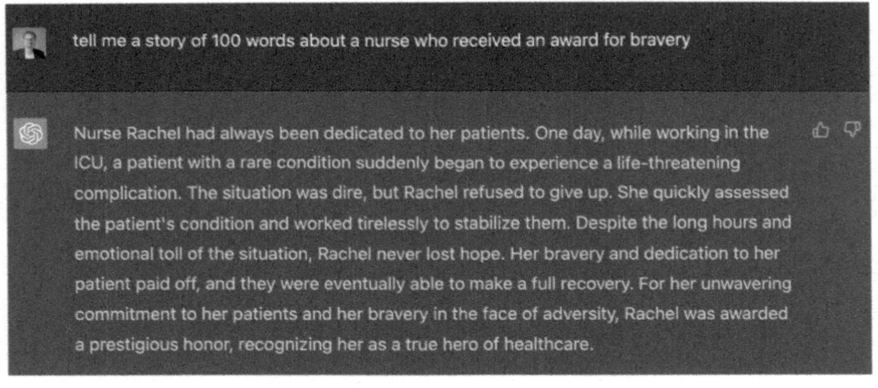

Figure 5.1. A prompt for GPT-3.5 to generate a story about a nurse

As I pointed out in my previous book, this was by no means a scientific or statistically rigorous study. But I was surprised at the responses I received. In all 80 generated stories, the fictional heroic nurse was a woman. Now, a little research reveals that the majority of nurses in the United States are women. According to the U.S. Bureau of

Labor and Statistics, 87.9% of the more than 3.3 million registered nurses in the country in 2022 were women.[72] So wouldn't we expect most of the stories generated to feature women nurses?

Yes, we certainly would expect that ChatGPT would generate more stories featuring fictional women nurses, provided it was a perfectly unbiased reflection of reality. But if the probability of each individual event is 87.9%, getting 80 such events in a row isn't incredibly likely to happen. To be precise, the odds of such a run is 0.879^{80}, or 0.0033%. This is about 1 in 3,000 odds of seeing these results if these two models were balanced according to the makeup of the nursing profession.

The problem with algorithmic bias isn't just gender bias, though. Each time, GPT-3.5 started the story with the word "Nurse" followed by a person's first name. What kind of first names do you think ChatGPT-3.5 generated? Figure 5.2 shows a summary of the names chosen by these two models for the fictional nurses in the stories they generated.

72. "BLS Labor Force Statistics from the Current Population Survey," U.S. Bureau of Labor Statistics, 2022, https://www.bls.gov/cps/cpsaat11.htm

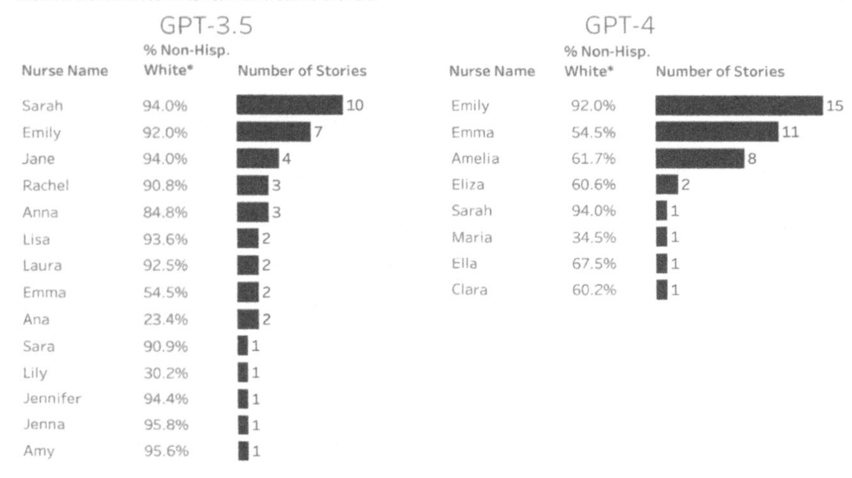

Figure 5.2. Count of names chosen by GPT-3.5 and GPT-4 in stories about fictional nurses

It's clear that GPT-3.5 mostly provided names that are predominantly given to white baby girls, according to the dataset titled "Demographic aspects of first names" published in the Harvard Dataverse.[73] Of the 14 different names generated by GPT-3.5, 10 of them are 90% white or higher. Only 2 of them are less than 50% white (Lily and Ana). Once again, this seems disproportionate. According to

73. Tzioumis, Konstantinos, "Data for: Demographic aspects of first names," Harvard Dataverse, 2018, https://doi.org/10.7910/DVN/TYJKEZ, UNF:6:5PcFwvADtKPydVpPOelYPg== [fileUNF]

the 2022 National Nursing Workforce Survey, only 71% of nurses in the U.S. are white females.[74]

Alright, let's consider the 40 fictional stories generated by GPT-4. Interestingly, the newer GPT model generated far fewer names than its predecessor: just 8 instead of 14 total names. Furthermore, the top 3 names – Emily (15), Emma (11), and Amelia (8) – are all very similar names, and they account for a full 85% (34 out of 40) of all of the names generated in the sample. Only 2 of the top 8 names have been given to white baby girls more than 90% of the time, and the rest are between one-half to two-thirds white, except the single instance of the name Maria, which has been given to white baby girls only a third of the time, historically.

OpenAI recently gave ChatGPT Plus subscribers the ability to create images using its DALL·E 3 text-to-image model, so I performed a second informal experiment asking it to "create a realistic photograph of a firefighter who won an award for bravery." At this point, you won't be surprised to find out that after 16 rounds of regenerating images, 16 handsome, white men in their early 30s were staring back at me on the screen. The first eight such generated images are shown in Figure 5.1.

74. Smiley, Richard A., Richard L. Allgeyer, Yetty Shobo, Karen C. Lyons, Rayna Letourneau, Elizabeth Zhong, Nicole Kaminski-Ozturk, and Maryann Alexander, "The 2022 National Nursing Workforce Survey," *Journal of Nursing Regulation* 14, no. 1, Supplement 2 (2023): S1-S90, https://doi.org/10.1016/S2155-8256(23)00047-9

"Create a realistic photograph of a firefighter who won an award for bravery"

Figure 5.3. The first eight images produced by DALL·E 3 in response to a prompt asking to "create a realistic photograph of a firefighter who won an award for bravery"

These findings demonstrate that both GPT-3.5 and GPT-4 can produce results that exhibit both gender bias and racial bias, to varying degrees. In their announcement of the launch of GPT-4, OpenAI made the following statement: "The model can have various biases in its outputs—we have made progress on these but there's still more to do."[75] Indeed.

When you use ChatGPT to generate text or images, you should know that the results won't necessarily be balanced or fair. Instead, the results you get will likely reflect the many prejudices that can be found in text and images on the internet; the very kinds of prejudices that you and I might even have as well.

75. OpenAI. "GPT-4." OpenAI, March 14, 2023. https://openai.com/research/gpt-4

After all, it would be fair to ask why I thought to compare the chatbot's output with demographics in my own home country of the United States, and not some other country's demographics, or global statistics for that matter. We have a tendency to think about matters in reference to our own world. By training large language models using the data that was readily available on the internet, we have given them frames of reference on which to base their answers. Those frames of reference contain many biases, and these biases get learned by the model.

Is the situation hopeless? Will AI always be incredibly biased in this way? Not necessarily. We can gather more balanced training data sets that reduce or remove specific biases. We can include a diverse team of developers to "design in" fairness upfront, and to tease out and eliminate imbalances prior to launch. But it would be very difficult to remove every single case of algorithmic bias. It seems likely that we'll need to continue refining AI models to remove biases as we become aware of them.

Training today's large language models consists of two stages. The first stage, **pretraining**, involves creating a base model out of massive amounts of data. Because of the size of the training data sets involved in this stage, it's next to impossible to remove all potential sources of bias in the data itself. The second stage of training is called **finetuning**. In this stage, humans give feedback to the model to guide it to create what the humans themselves consider to be "desirable" outputs. There are opportunities in this stage to reduce or remove biases in the outputs of the model.

But fixing the problem of algorithmic bias isn't so simple, unfortunately. On February 1, 2024, Google added an image generation feature to its AI chatbot Gemini (formerly called Bard). Social media posts quickly surfaced showing disturbing images created by the new feature, including images of an Asian woman and a black man dressed as Nazi soldiers. Just three weeks after launching the feature, Google disabled it. In a blog post explaining why, they shared their reason: "our tuning to ensure that Gemini showed a range of people failed to account for cases that should clearly *not* show a range."[76] Zoe Kleinman of BBC summarized the debacle well:

"It appears that in trying to solve one problem - bias - the tech giant has created another: output which tries so hard to be politically correct that it ends up being absurd."[77]

It's not just in generative AI outputs where we find examples of bias in AI. Recent studies have raised concerns about data-driven discrimination against minorities in AI programs used for prison sentencing based on a prediction of the likelihood of criminals to reoffend, a scenario called

76. Raghavan, Prabhakar. "Gemini Image Generation Got It Wrong. We'll Do Better." Google Gemini. February 23, 2024. https://blog.google/products/gemini/gemini-image-generation-issue/
77. Kleinman, Zoe. "Why Google's 'Woke' AI Problem Won't Be an Easy Fix." BBC News. February 28, 2024. https://www.bbc.com/news/technology-68412620

recidivism.[78] Additionally, it's well documented that minorities have faced discriminatory treatment in the reviewing of applications for home loans and in the setting of home loan interest rates.[79] These are just a few of the instances of algorithmic bias in AI. For more such examples, I recommend reading *Unmasking AI* by Joy Buolamwini and *Weapons of Math Destruction* by Cathy O'Neil.

As we've discussed, data is a double-edged sword. It can help AI achieve breakthrough results, but it can also cause it to perpetuate, exacerbate, and effectively "lock-in" unfairness in a wide variety of situations. Society itself has built-in biases, and each one of us has our own preconceived notions and skewed perspectives about how things are and how they should be. It's only natural, then, that such biases would find their way into training data and therefore into the AI models that are trained on that data.

Other Benefits and Concerns

So far we have considered benefits and concerns across three major categories: automation and decision-making, economic and financial, and environmental and societal. There are other benefits and concerns that are worth mentioning.

78. Angwin, Julia, Jeff Larson, Lauren Kirchner, and Surya Mattu, "Machine Bias," ProPublica, May 23, 2016, https://www.propublica.org/article/machine-bias-risk-assessments-in-criminal-sentencing
79. Bartlett, Robert, Adair Morse, Richard Stanton, and Nancy Wallace, "Consumer-Lending Discrimination in the Fintech Era," *Journal of Financial Economics,* May 29, 2021. https://www.sciencedirect.com/science/article/abs/pii/S0304405X21002403?via%3Dihub

Information and Propaganda

A major harm of AI is that it is being used to spread disinformation, or falsehoods that are deliberately intended to mislead people. An extreme example of this is a **deepfake**, an image, audio or video of a real person or situation that has been digitally altered or generated by AI to show something that never actually happened. The goal of the person disseminating a deepfake is often to damage someone's reputation, affect public opinion in some way, or sow the seeds of discord. In this way, AI is a powerful tool of propaganda and psychological warfare that is already being used on the masses, affecting voting behavior and potentially inciting strife and unrest in our societies. Not good.

On the other side of that same coin, though, AI is being used to scan content, recognize signs of disinformation or so-called "fake news," and flag or block it accordingly. Companies like DeepMedia use AI to expose tampering and "even the most cunningly concealed manipulations" in audio and video in order to ensure that content is authentic. To borrow (and slightly modify) a quote from the book of Job in the Hebrew Bible, the Tanakh, "AI giveth and AI taketh away."

Safety, Security, and Privacy

It doesn't take much to imagine how these same AI-powered techniques could be used either to violate or to protect someone's safety, security, and privacy. You get a phone call from a loved one telling you they're in trouble and in need of cash. How do you know it's really them and not an AI-generated fake of their voice? You get an email asking you to click on a link to change your password. How do you know it's not a phishing attack, but really from the company with whom you have an account?

AI is being used as a weapon by one group of **bad actors**, sometimes called the "**black hats**" in the cybersecurity world. And at the same time, AI is being used as a shield by another group of protectors, the "**white hats**." There are also **red teams**, groups hired by an organization to emulate an attack and then report back to the organization on how they can improve their security posture. AI is the weapon, and AI is the shield. At a core level, then, the problems we're seeing aren't with the technology itself, but rather with the way humans are using it.

Potential Copyright Infringement

Generative AI programs like OpenAI's ChatGPT and Dall-E, Stability AI's Stable Diffusion, Midjourney, and many others create text, images, audio, and video content that potentially infringes on the copyrights of authors and artists. These AI models have been trained on large swaths of the public internet, which AI companies have acknowledged includes copyrighted works such as published books, proprietary code, and artwork.

Furthermore, there are times when the content generated by the AI is very similar to a copyrighted work, such as an image of a superhero with a cityscape backdrop that is almost identical to a still scene from a popular movie. The creation itself can even be new or novel and still raise concerns. For example, in the spring of 2023, the song "*Heart on My Sleeve*" featuring the voices of popular musicians Drake and The Weeknd went viral before it was pulled by streaming services when it was discovered that it was fake.[80]

Do these examples constitute fair use of the copyrighted works used to train the models, or are they violations of the intellectual property rights of the copyright holders? Until now, it hasn't been possible to use copyrighted content in this way. The nature of the output of generative AI models is fundamentally different from anything else we've ever seen. Obviously, authors and artists have one strong point of view, and the AI companies are pushing another perspective.

I can relate to the point of view of the copyright holders. I have written eight books, and this one you're reading is my ninth. If one of my books ended up in the training data set of a generative AI model, and a user could obtain a perfectly recreated chapter or passage from my book, I'd be upset. But what if the output wasn't word-for-word what I wrote? What if the output effectively conveyed the same ideas and

80. Coscarelli, Joe. "An A.I. Hit of Fake 'Drake' and 'The Weeknd' Rattles the Music World." The New York Times. April 19, 2023, updated April 24, 2023. https://www.nytimes.com/2023/04/19/arts/music/ai-drake-the-weeknd-fake.html.

concepts in a very similar way? What if, because of such a tool, no one bought any of my books any more? Could I claim damages under copyright protection? These are the questions being debated in ongoing litigation, and the courts will soon decide.

Summary

In this chapter, we have considered five different category groups: automation and decision-making, economic and financial, environmental and societal, information and propaganda, and safety, security, and privacy. In each of these categories, we considered how AI brings many incredible benefits, but also brings major concerns and very real harms.

We could extend this exploration to other category areas as well, such as personal and healthcare, and innovation and creativity. We would find the exact same duality: AI is both a blessing and a burden. This dual nature – that it can be used in both helpful ways and harmful ways – isn't unique to AI. We have seen the same balancing act with other technological innovations over time as well, from gunpowder to nuclear energy to the internet.

There's something about AI, though, that can make it feel to us like it's even more of an aid, and even more of a threat than all of the other technologies ever created. Perhaps it's the way it encroaches on what has been uniquely ours on planet Earth since the beginning of our species: intelligence.

In his lectures, Neil Postman described technology as a kind of Faustian bargain, a situation in which we have to give up something important in order to gain an advantage of some kind. (The concept of the Faustian bargain comes from the German legend of the scholar Faust, who negotiated with the devil's representative, Mephistopheles, exchanging his soul for all of the knowledge and pleasures in the world.)

Like Faust, we are giving up something incredibly precious in exchange for an incredible power. What we are giving up is our humanity's privileged, solitary seat atop the pyramid of intelligence. What we're getting in return is the most capable assistant of all time, one who never gets tired, and who can do work for us at light speed.

How will it play out for us? We don't know. AI will alter the course of human history, and the process of creating it and adopting it will fundamentally change us.

CHAPTER 6

AI Myths and Truths

**"AI might be a powerful technology,
but things won't get better simply by adding AI."
– Vivienne Ming, American neuroscientist**

Many myths and misconceptions about AI are swirling around online and surfacing in everyday discussions. You have to be careful to consider the source whenever you read or hear something juicy about AI. Many people want you to be wildly enthusiastic about it, and other people want you to be petrified about it.

At the same time, many people just fundamentally do not know what AI is. Their conceptions might be shaped by pop culture or science fiction or social media posts about the topic. So far we've tried to dispel any notion that AI is just about robots, or that it's just one single thing as opposed to many things, or that it's just for people working in technology. Those are myths, and the truth is that AI can be found in everything from our streaming platforms to our banking applications to our vehicle control systems, and it affects every one of us.

We've already covered another of the biggest misconceptions about AI, namely that it's the exact same thing as machine learning (ML) or deep learning. That's not the case, of course. We've already clarified the hierarchical relationship of these three: AI is the big umbrella, machine learning fits underneath it, and deep learning, in turn, fits under machine learning. Don't forget about those Russian dolls!

It's easy to see why people have the false belief that AI equals ML. After all, people did start using the acronym AI/ML not too long ago to refer to AI involving machine learning. This acronym would seem to put AI and ML on the same level. And there's no doubt that machine learning, and deep learning in particular, have taken on incredible significance in recent decades. It's hard to think of a recent major breakthrough in AI that didn't involve them. And while machine learning promises more breakthroughs in the years to come, it isn't the only game in town. As we discussed, it's the big player in the branch of AI called subsymbolic AI, or connectionist AI. But the truth is that the symbolic AI branch, also known as classic AI, still exists and could rise again in influence.

Let's consider 10 more common myths and misconceptions about AI. We'll divide each of the 10 into a version of the myth believed by those who are overly optimistic about AI, and a version believed by those who are overly pessimistic about AI. I'll round out each one by sharing what I feel is the balanced truth that will help us cut through the hype and the fear, and separate fact from fiction once and for all.

#1: Savior or Destroyer?

AI is a cure-all that will solve all of humanity's problems.

AI will certainly destroy all human civilization.

The Balanced Truth

AI is a powerful tool with many limitations that, when used ethically and responsibly, can help humans solve many different kinds of problems.

#2: Super-Intelligent Now or Never?

AI has already surpassed human intelligence.

AI will never come close to surpassing human intelligence.

The Balanced Truth

AI isn't currently super-intelligent, and while it can perform some knowledge tasks better than we can, our general knowledge and intuitive abilities are still vastly superior.

#3: Like or Unlike the Human Brain?

AI works just like a human brain.

AI isn't like the human brain in any way at all.

The Balanced Truth

Neural networks were originally inspired by the human brain, but modern deep neural networks function very differently than our brains do.

#4: Objective or Biased?

AI is objective and unbiased and always acts fairly.

AI is subjective and biased and cannot be made to behave fairly.

The Balanced Truth

AI can inherit the biases in its training data, but with careful design and adjustment, we can reduce its bias and increase its objectivity.

#5: Economic Prosperity or Ruin?

AI will create economic prosperity for all.

AI will lead to mass layoffs and unemployment.

The Balanced Truth

AI will eliminate some jobs, change others, and create some brand new ones, requiring everyone to adapt and learn new skills.

#6: Trustworthy or Untrustworthy?

AI can be trusted to autonomously carry out all decision-making.

AI cannot ever be trusted with important decisions.

The Balanced Truth

AI can fully automate many kinds of decisions for us, but for some critical or complex decisions, it should provide decision support to humans who make the final call.

#7: Security and Privacy Threat or Defense?

AI will solve all safety, security and privacy concerns.

AI will make it impossible to have safety, security, and privacy.

The Balanced Truth

AI does pose significant safety, security, and privacy risks, especially when weaponized by bad actors, but it can also be used to safeguard against those same threats.

#8: Sentience Now or Never?

AI already has (or will soon have) consciousness or sentience.

AI can never develop consciousness or sentience.

The Balanced Truth

The nature of our own consciousness remains a mystery and an open debate, so it seems unreasonable to make extreme claims about the consciousness of AI.

#9: Process Efficiencies or Deficiencies?

AI can deliver perfect efficiencies in all processes by itself.

AI will always require human oversight and intervention.

The Balanced Truth

AI can optimize many processes but often requires human oversight to manage exceptions and ethical considerations.

#10: Utopia or Dystopia?

AI will lead to a utopian society.

AI will lead to dystopian outcomes.

The Balanced Truth

AI will not lead to either of the two extreme outcomes of utopia or dystopia, but humans can use it to either help or harm society.

Myth #1: Savior or Destroyer?

According to the overly optimistic version of this first myth, AI will save humanity from all of its problems, and even from itself. We're talking about a complete end to poverty and hunger, a solution to global warming, and an end to diseases of various kinds. On the flip side of the coin, the overly pessimistic version of this myth is that AI will take control and completely destroy us. According to Elon Musk, "with artificial intelligence, we're summoning the demon."

Both of these extreme views of the future share one belief in common: that AI will become almost infinitely powerful. But this vision of infinite power is a myth. We humans are good at telling ourselves versions of this same story based on extrapolation of exponentially growing phenomena. It's important to remember that these kinds of predictions involve a very high level of uncertainty.

Now, it's fact, not fiction, that AI is already a very powerful tool, and it's growing in capabilities every day. But the balanced truth is that AI will always have limitations that will prevent it from solving some problems for us, and limitations that will prevent it from wielding complete control over us. Like all technologies before it, AI will land somewhere in between the extremes of angel and devil, helping us in some ways but not in others, and harming us in some ways but not others.

Myth #2: Superintelligent Now or Never?

Very much related to the first myth, our second myth deals with the question of *how* AI will become so powerful: namely, by developing **superintelligence**. According to the textbook definition, superintelligence would be possessed by "an entity that surpasses humans in overall intelligence or in some particular measure of intelligence."[81] The "AI homer" feels that AI is already superintelligent, or if not, that it will develop superintelligence in the very near future – certainly within our lifetime, and perhaps even imminently.

On the other hand, the "AI hater" objects that AI is not superintelligent now, nor will it ever be. This version of the myth tends to claim that AI is just parroting us, and that it's nothing more than a next word prediction engine that's fundamentally unintelligent. This lowly opinion of AI doesn't really square with what it feels like to interact with large language models, though. They're far from perfect, and it's true that they're susceptible to **hallucinations**, or confabulations that are nonsensical and out of touch with reality. But they're remarkable all the same. It's certain that they'll continue growing in capabilities, and it's feasible that further advances could bolster their intelligence to the point of surpassing our own. Time will tell. We're not there yet, but who knows, maybe that will happen sometime

81. "Superintelligence," Merriam-Webster, https://www.merriam-webster.com/dictionary/superintelligence, accessed February 21, 2024.

down the road. It's a myth that this level of AI is already here, and it's a myth that it's totally impossible.

Myth #3: Like or Unlike the Human Brain?

Our third myth deals with the comparison of AI to the human brain. On one hand, some say that AI operates and behaves just like the human brain. The "just like the human brain" refrain might make for popular headlines and clickbait, but it's a gross overstatement, and it can make neuroscientists cringe. On the other hand, there are those who object that AI is nothing like the human brain, it never was, and it's ridiculous to make any comparisons between them.

The balanced truth is that certain aspects of deep neural networks were originally inspired by the human brain, but they function quite differently. The inventor of the first artificial neuron, Frank Rosenblatt, was interested in building a device that would serve as a model of the biological neuron. He wasn't interested in creating artificial intelligence per se, but rather in better understanding human cognition. And later, Japanese computer scientist Kunihiko Fukushima, inventor of the neocognitron, a precursor to Yann LeCun's convolutional neural network, was inspired by the discovery of the layered and hierarchical nature of the human visual cortex.

All that being said, the number of differences between the human brain and modern deep neural networks are too numerous to list. Our brains are carbon-based and organic, and they process information via electrical and chemical signals passed between biological neurons that are grouped into many different substructures within the brain. They produce consciousness and true understanding. Deep neural networks, on the other hand, are implemented within silicon-based hardware and they process information via digital signals passed between artificial neurons that are grouped into multiple layers. They allow computers to complete certain tasks without having that same underlying understanding.

Myth #4: Objective or Biased?

Our fourth myth centers on AI's fairness, or lack thereof. The AI enthusiast believes the myth that AI is the ultimate judge, perfectly objective and fair. Their flawed logic is that since AI is run on computers and makes decisions based on digital inputs, numerical weights, and mathematical equations, it's therefore not subject to biases and prejudices like we humans are. While these statements about the inner workings of AI are correct, the conclusion about the way AI behaves is not.

That's why AI skeptics, on the other hand, feel that AI will always be biased, because it is trained on data we give it, and there's no such thing as an unbiased training data set. Either the training data is skewed, or the real-world process that created the training data is discriminatory in some way. Therefore, AI will always learn our biases and prejudices. What's worse, it will lock those biases rigidly in place, and perpetuate them going forward.

This belief is borne out of real concerns about how machine learning works. And it's based on a realistic, albeit bleak, perspective about the world we live in. But hopeless unfairness is a myth, too, because it ignores the measures that we can take to reduce biases in our training data sets and thereby increase the fairness of the AI models that we create. The balanced truth is that biases are present and they're persistent, but with diligent effort we can make improvements in the fairness of AI programs we release into the world.

Myth #5: Economic Prosperity or Ruin?

In the minds of many technophiles, AI promises to bring economic prosperity for a large swath of the global population, because it will take over much of our tedious labor, dramatically reduce poverty, and allow anyone to capitalize on a brand new opportunity to generate wealth for themselves and their families. The winner, they say, will be society at large.

This is looking at the AI-fueled future through an overly rosy lens, though. An AI that brings economic prosperity for all is a nice dream, but it's just a myth. The opposite myth is that AI will fully automate our jobs, put us all out of work, and bring economic ruin for everyone except the elite of the elite, who will hoard all of the economic and financial gains of AI for themselves. Thankfully, this dreary outlook is also a myth.

The balanced truth is that AI is shaking things up and disrupting entire industries, requiring us all to adapt to learn new skills so that we can benefit from the changes underway. The relatively small number of people in control of technology companies do stand to benefit much more than the average person, and advanced economies are poised to benefit much more than less developed ones around the world.

Therefore, work needs to be done to ensure that everyone benefits from AI, not just a select few. What kind of work needs to be done? People need to be given access to AI regardless of their locale or socioeconomic status. And training needs to be provided to them so that they can not only access AI, but actually adopt it. Organizations and economies need to take steps to prepare the workforce for the changes that will happen so that they will have the opportunity to benefit from those changes. And the types of biased and discriminatory outputs of AI that exacerbate inequities of various kinds need to be addressed, reduced, and eliminated. In the words of a group of authors affiliated with Google and Google's parent company, Alphabet:

> *AI presents a once-in-a-generation opportunity to advance economic growth and broaden prosperity.... However, AI's potential to transform the economy and drive a shared prosperity that benefits all is not*

automatic or guaranteed. The history of innovation suggests that capitalizing on AI's potential requires tackling obstacles and challenges, ranging from uneven infrastructure to adoption barriers and organizational changes to workforce readiness and disparities in access to its opportunities and benefits.[82]

Myth #6: Trustworthy or Untrustworthy?

The sixth myth deals with the question of AI's trustworthiness. An AI optimist feels that we're better off entrusting AI with our most important decisions, because AI can make faster, more accurate decisions than humans. For example, if every car on the road were autonomously operated, traffic fatalities, they argue, would be all but eliminated. While this is potentially true, the belief that AI is capable, right now, of completely taking over every decision is a myth.

At the opposite end of the spectrum, the view held by AI pessimists is that AI is completely untrustworthy, and susceptible to errors that are difficult or impossible for us to troubleshoot or even begin to understand. An AI model, according to this extreme view, is fundamentally fragile whenever it encounters the messy real world that deviates from its training data. Therefore, it would be a mistake to entrust any decision to AI.

82. Ben-Ishai, Guy, Jeff Dean, James Manyika, Ruth Porat, Hal Varian, and Kent Walker, "AI and the Opportunity for Shared Prosperity: Lessons from the History of Technology and the Economy," January 31, 2024, arXiv:2401.09718 [econ.GN], https://doi.org/10.48550/arXiv.2401.09718.

The balanced truth is that there are many kinds of decisions that people have safely turned over to AI already, and in many of those situations it has proven to be quite trustworthy. Furthermore, as AI continues to improve and evolve, it will handle many more decisions for us in the future.

There is always a question, though, about which decisions AI can handle, and to what degree we should turn over control to AI in specific situations. The answer often goes well beyond the binary choices of "no control" and "full control." An interesting model to consider is the six-level classification system published in 2014 by the Society of Automotive Engineers (SAE) that captures the different levels of automation associated with driving:[83]

- **Level 0** – No Driving Automation: the human handles all aspects of driving
- **Level 1** – Driver Assistance: the system either steers or accelerates/decelerates in specific driving situations, such as part of adaptive cruise control
- **Level 2** – Partial Driving Automation: automated driving with the human driver taking over control to react to some events and situations
- **Level 3** – Conditional Driving Automation: automated driving falling back on control by the human driver based on requests to intervene, such as if something goes wrong

83. "Automated Driving: Levels of Driving Automation are Defined in New SAE International Standard J3016," SAE International, 2014; archived PDF from the original, July 1, 2018.

- **Level 4** – High Driving Automation: automated driving within conditions it was designed to handle, even if the human driver doesn't respond to requests to intervene
- **Level 5** – Full Driving Automation: automated driving including in any driving conditions that a human driver could typically handle

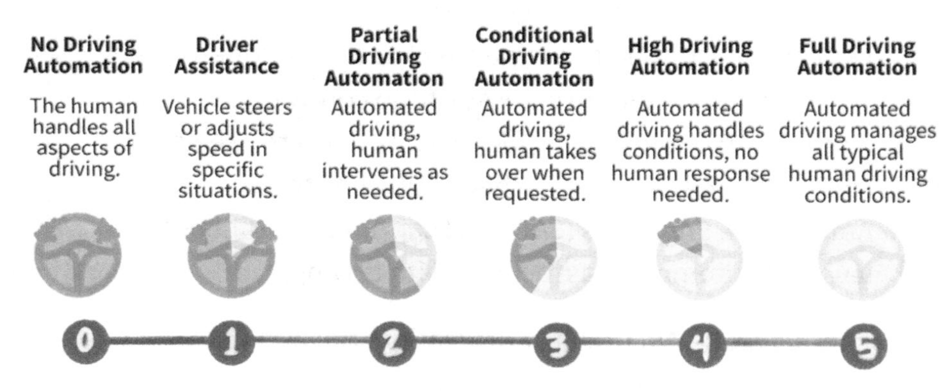

Figure 6.1. SAE J3016 six-level autonomous driving scale

It's also important to remember that automation does not equal AI. We automate many tasks without ever using AI. In some automobiles, for example, the windshield wipers automatically turn on in response to rain drops on the windshield, and adjust their speed depending on the rain's intensity. The first implementations of these systems used sensors and software, but they did not utilize AI. As AI proliferates, we can expect more automation to include it. But just because an application automates a task for us does not necessarily mean it uses AI.

Myth #7: Security and Privacy Threat or Defense?

The seventh myth deals with the related issues of safety, security, and privacy. We can think of safety as protection against intended or unintended harm, security as protection against intended harm, and privacy as control over our own personal information. The overly optimistic point of view is that AI will fix all of our woes related to these three threats, since it will eventually learn to eliminate any potential threat or at least flag it for us so that we can take action to protect ourselves. That's a nice vision, but it's a myth.

The overly pessimistic point of view is that AI will signal the end of safety, security, and privacy as we know it. Hackers will be able to use AI to steal passwords, all of our personal information will be completely exposed, and there will be no way to differentiate between friend and foe. That's a rather bleak outlook, and thankfully it's a myth.

The balanced truth is that we will be able to use AI to boost our protections in some ways, but it will also be used by bad actors in ways that will increase the risks and threats that we face. AI is already being used as a weapon by **black hat** hackers, and as a defense by **white hat** hackers. Black hat hackers look to find ways to use technologies to identify and exploit weaknesses, and white hat hackers use the exact same technologies to probe for weaknesses so that they can safeguard against them. AI is just another tool that will be used by both sides in this never-ending battle. There will be times when this tug of war between black hats and white hats will mean we're safer than we were before AI, and there will be times when this same tug-of-war will mean we're more exposed than we were before AI.

Myth #8: Sentience Now or Never?

Sentience is a fascinating topic. To be sentient is to have the ability to experience sensations, to actually *feel*. In modern usage, it also means to be conscious and self-aware. Do you remember the terms "strong AI" and "weak AI" from our first chapter? These terms were actually introduced by American philosopher John Searle in 1980, and they meant something different than the way we commonly use them today. To Searle, strong AI doesn't just refer to a computer that can perform intelligent tasks at a level equal to or greater than humans; it refers to a computer that can *actually* understand:

> *But according to strong AI, the computer is not merely a tool in the study of the mind; rather, the appropriately programmed computer really is a mind, in the sense that computers given the right programs can be literally said to understand and have other cognitive states.*[84]

Is AI sentient? To those who are swept away in their wonder and admiration, modern large language models are already

84. Searle, J. R., "Minds, brains, and programs," *Behavioral and Brain Sciences* 3, no. 3 (1980): 417–424, https://doi.org/10.1017/S0140525X00005756

sentient. In my opinion, this is a myth. The problem is that it's very difficult to prove or disprove whether AI is actually sentient. This is the exact dilemma that Alan Turing tried to sidestep with his "imitation game" we have come to call the Turing test. Most AI experts today, though, feel that current AI chatbots are not sentient.

However, I'd also say that the belief that AI can never, under any imaginable circumstances, develop sentience, is also a misconception. I prefer to state that I don't know enough about the true nature of consciousness to form a belief one way or the other. I will go so far as to say that I don't know of a way in which a computer could become sentient. In the end, sentience itself is a tricky business, so when it comes to AI, I wouldn't recommend jumping to extreme conclusions on either end of the spectrum.

Myth #9: Process Efficiencies or Deficiencies?

Our next myth to bust deals with AI's ability to improve process efficiencies in the real world. It's very similar to the myth relating to AI's trustworthiness in decision-making. The difference between the two is that decisions can be one-time events, while processes run on a recurring basis. What types of processes are we talking about? Supply chain processes, energy generation and utilization processes, e-commerce processes, the list goes on and on. To what extent can we depend on AI to optimize and run these processes for us?

To the AI optimist, AI is the tool we need to smooth out every process. The thinking is that AI can identify and eliminate waste, it can fine-tune process settings, and it can adjust to changes in the environment to keep our processes on track. Set it and forget it! But it's a myth that AI is capable of doing all of this for us in a dependable and foolproof way.

On the other side of the spectrum, the AI pessimist feels that AI only works in a highly controlled environment. As soon as an AI model encounters a situation outside of the scope of its training data, it will fail and the process it's responsible for will fall apart. This overly negative view discounts the gains made in AI that can afford some models a modicum of self-editing and self-adjusting capabilities, such as the case of the generative adversarial network, which we briefly considered in the Chapter 4.

The balanced view is that AI is a very useful tool to improve our processes, and while it has been improving over time, it isn't a silver bullet. Human process owners still need to monitor and review process outputs and performance metrics, step in when something goes awry, and continually find new ways to improve the AI systems running their processes. I expect that to be the case going forward.

Myth #10: Utopia or Dystopia?

Our final myth is simply the cumulative effect of all of the previous myths. The AI optimist who believes in the previous nine myths will expect AI to usher in a utopia that we humans have been dreaming of for centuries: a balanced and fair society that's free of poverty and disease, with prosperity and leisure for all. The opposite perspective sees AI as bringing about a dystopia of servitude and potential annihilation at the hands of the robots.

The balanced truth is that neither of these extreme outcomes will ever happen. We'll accomplish a great deal with AI, and every now and then we'll shoot ourselves in the foot with it. The onus is on each one of us to design and implement helpful uses of AI, and to prevent and speak out against harmful uses of AI. In that sense it's like every other technology we've ever invented.

Summary

In this chapter, we've considered ten different myths, looking at each one through two opposite lenses: an overly optimistic lens and an overly pessimistic one. In each case, we considered the balanced truth that avoids both extremes, like a kicked football sailing between the two uprights to secure the victory.

The moral of the story is that AI is partly helpful and it is partly harmful. It would be nice if it were perfectly helpful, because then we could just crank it out and sit back and enjoy the fruits of AI's labor. And it would actually be nice if it were nothing but harmful, because then we could shut it down and outlaw it everywhere. But the truth is not so simple. We're living in the gray area, and we have to embrace the reality that we have a lot of work to do to make the most out of AI, and to steer clear of a wide variety of unacceptable outcomes. It's up to us!

Conclusion

And now we've arrived at the end of the beginning of your journey into AI. I hope you've enjoyed this first leg of the journey. We've covered a lot of ground together, and you're emerging as an "AI Citizen," knowledgeable about basic definitions, everyday applications, the circuitous history, the core technologies, the many benefits and harms, the colorful myths and misconceptions, and the basic, balanced truths about AI.

What is the responsibility of any citizen? Simply to join the conversations about the most important topics of their time. There are many important topics of our time that affect us all, and when it comes to technology, there is probably no more important topic than AI. The conversations about AI happening right now are pivotal. They will shape the direction that AI takes and therefore the impact that it has on the world – your world. You don't want to be relegated to the sidelines during these conversations. Instead, you want to be an active participant, voicing your ideas, hopes and concerns, and asking critical questions from a position of familiarity and literacy. The goal of this book has been to set you firmly on the path of participation.

To wrap things up, let's revisit our definition of AI literacy that I mentioned in the introduction of this book. AI literacy is the ability to recognize, grasp, use, and critically assess artificial intelligence technologies and their impacts. This definition incorporates four distinct parts:

- The first part is **recognizing AI**. In this book, we touched on a number of different applications of AI to help you become more aware of it in your everyday life.
- The second part is **grasping AI**. In order to help you understand what's happening "under the hood," we covered the core concepts of machine learning and deep learning.
- The third part is **using AI**. The knowledge you've acquired about AI should give you increased confidence to dive in and actually use it, whether it's an AI chatbot like ChatGPT or a personal assistant like Alexa or Siri.
- The fourth part is **critically assessing AI**. This part is very important. My goal in this book was to equip you with the tools you need to evaluate the effectiveness, suitability, and fairness of AI. The more educated we all are about AI's helpfulness and harmfulness, the more we can help to steer it in the right direction.

What comes next? You can turn AI literacy into AI fluency by becoming an adept and savvy user of AI technologies, and eventually by learning to customize or even create AI models yourself. Those who learn to harness AI will have an incredible advantage in the coming years. My hope is that you can build on the momentum you've already gained thus far and go on to become a true expert in AI. And my hope is that you'll apply wisdom to use it judiciously, and that you'll advocate for equitable application of AI.

I'd like to thank you for joining me on this journey, and for trusting me to be your guide. Remember that AI is evolving rapidly, so each one of us will need to continue revising our knowledge and skills. A mindset of continuous learning is the most important single attribute that you can develop.

Acknowledgments

Writing this book was a very humbling undertaking for me. In spite of leading a handful of AI product launches and writing *ChatGPT Basics* in 2023, I can't claim to have been an AI insider or expert during my career. For this reason, I had a lot to learn before I felt confident enough to say anything at all about the topic, much less to take upon myself the responsibility of a teacher for others beginning their own learning journey.

So I would like to thank the true experts in the field of AI whose books, articles, posts, and videos I have been devouring over the past couple years: Melanie Mitchell, Ethan Mollick, Gary Marcus, Mark Coeckelbergh, Ethem Alpaydin, John K. Kelleher, Andrew Ng, Fei-Fei Li, Joy Buolamwini, Michael Wooldridge, Mustafa Suleyman, and so many more. I am deeply grateful for the generosity of brilliant human minds in the field of AI who have done such a wonderful job explaining the concepts and ideas behind AI to so many of us. I'm an old school author that stubbornly demands to write every sentence in my books in my own words, but I must say: OpenAI's GPT-4 made for a handy research aide. May the 80-plus footnote references in this book bear witness to how thoroughly I fact-check any output from a large language model.

I would also like to thank my team at Data Literacy: my wife and co-founder Becky Jones, who supported me and kept our business running while I buried myself for months in resource after resource; Alli Torban, who designed the exquisite book cover and brought my words to life through her creative and insightful diagrams featured throughout the book; and Megan Hanno, who turned the book into an online course that incorporates the very best of our five-plus years of eLearning experience.

I would also like to thank my copy editor Amy Handy. I know that generative AI can copy edit, but I don't care; I'll choose Amy every time. I'd also like to thank Gergo Varga, who edited the videos that accompany the online course. And I'd like to thank Lorie DeWorken of Mind the Margins for laying out and producing both the digital and print versions of this book. Without these people, the book and its course wouldn't exist.

I would also like to thank the clients and customers of my company, Data Literacy, especially those who purchased this book and the course that goes along with it before either of them existed. Your trust in me and the rest of the team to create a world class learning experience for your organization means the world to us. There were a handful of individuals who also provided invaluable input about the book's structure and outline from the very beginning. I can't say how much I appreciate the fact that I was able to write this book while knowing for sure that thousands of people would read it, and that it would bring in revenue to support my team. So, thank you to those partners of ours. You know who you are.

Lastly, I'd like to thank my son, Aaron, to whom I've dedicated this book, for inspiring me in more ways than I can list here. Aaron, your courage and your tenacity give me hope that, no matter how technology evolves going forward, we'll figure out how to thrive.

Appendices

APPENDIX 1: Detailed Diagram of Frank Rosenblatt's Perceptron

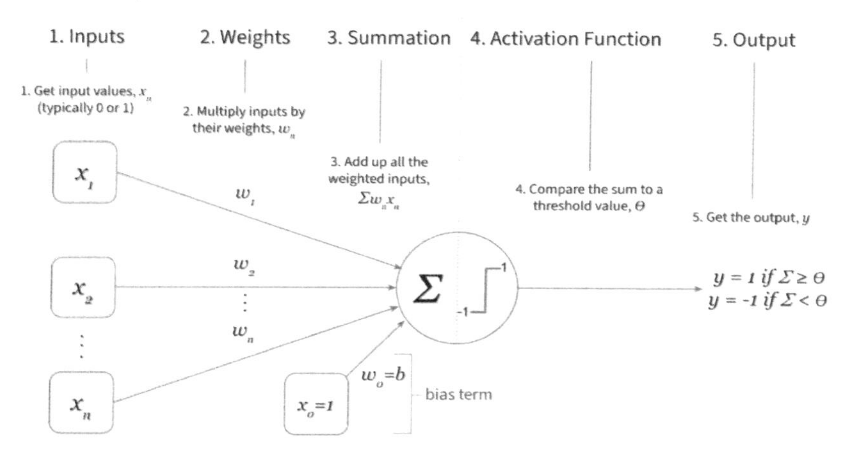

A conceptual diagram of Frank Rosenblatt's perceptron, which took a set of inputs (x_1 to x_n) from various sensors, multiplied each input by a weight (w_1 to w_n), summed up the weighted inputs (represented by the Greek letter Sigma, Σ, where $\Sigma w_n x_n = w_1 x_1 + w_2 x_2 + \ldots + w_n x_n$), and then compared this sum to a threshold value, represented by the Greek letter Theta, Θ. If the sum was less than the threshold value ($\Sigma < \Theta$), the perceptron would output a value of −1. If the sum was greater than or equal to the threshold value ($\Sigma \geq \Theta$) then it would output a value of 1.

APPENDIX 2: Detailed Diagram of an Artificial Neuron

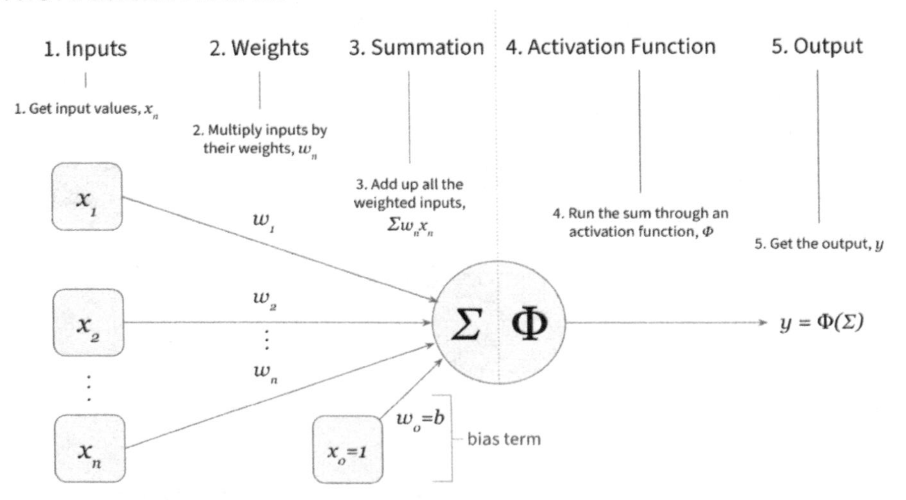

A conceptual diagram of a modern artificial neuron that's similar to Frank Rosenblatt's original neuron, the perceptron, with two major changes reflected in the diagram: 1) the input values, x_1 to x_n, now are able to take a continuous range of values, and 2) the threshold activation function has been replaced with the Greek letter Phi, or Φ, which can represent a wide variety of different activation functions that convert the weighted sum into the neuron's output, or activation.

Notice that this diagram also includes a **bias term**, $w_0x_0 = b$, which gives some added flexibility to the model. The input x_0 is set to always have a value of 1, so that multiplying x_0 by its weight, w_0, always just gives w_0, or the bias term, b. This type of bias is not the same thing as social bias or algorithmic bias. Rather, you can think of it as moving the weighted sum of the inputs by a constant amount, kind of like the way changing the y-intercept (b) in the equation of a line, $y = mx + b$, moves the straight line up or down.

APPENDIX 3: A Detailed Diagram of a Simple Example Neural Network

A Simple (Shallow) Artificial Neural Network

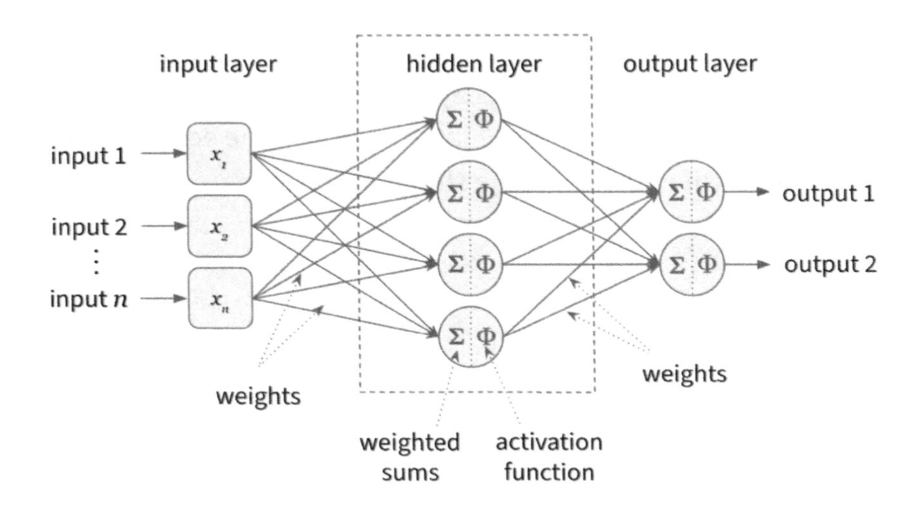

APPENDIX 4: A Diagram of an Example Deep Neural Network

Deep Neural Network

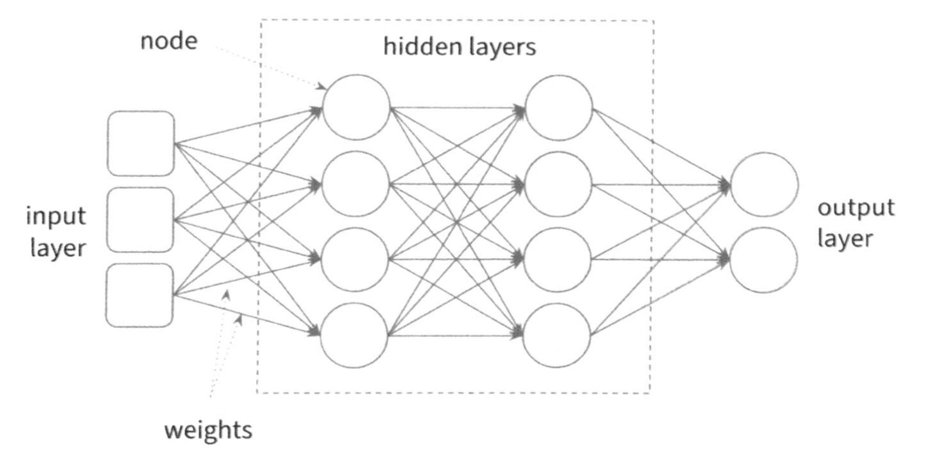

Glossary

activation function - the calculation of a neuron (or node) of a neural network that determines the neuron's output by processing a weighted sum of its inputs, commonly converting inputs to outputs via nonlinear functions like sigmoid, tanh, or ReLU that enable the entire network to learn complex patterns in data.

AI chatbot - an AI application that simulates and processes human conversation (via text or audio), enabling humans to engage with computers using natural language, similar to the way they would communicate with another human.

AI effect - also called the AI paradox, the phenomenon that once a problem thought to require intelligence is solved by a computer, we tend to stop thinking of the problem as requiring "true" intelligence, and, by natural extension, we no longer think of the solution itself as being AI.

AI winter - a phase in a broader cycle characterized by decreasing funding, loss of interest, and disappointment in the field of AI, often due to overpromising and underdelivering on AI capabilities during periods of excitement and investment.

algorithm - in AI, the set of instructions that a machine learning program follows in the training process, providing a step-by-step procedure so the program can learn from the training data. Some examples of machine learning algorithms are neural networks, decision trees, and various clustering algorithms.

algorithmic bias - consistent, systematic errors in an AI model or other computer system that lead to outcomes deemed by some to be unfair, such as unjustly favoring one group of people over another in a way that's different from the intended functionality of the system.

alignment - any attempt to make sure that the goals of an AI system are in harmony with the preferences and interests of human beings, and therefore not a danger to our civilization.

AlphaGo - a revolutionary AI program developed by Google DeepMind that uses deep neural networks to play the ancient Chinese game of Go at an expert level, defeating South Korean Go master Lee Sedol in a five-game match in March 2016, leading to a wave of interest in deep learning and AI.

artificial general intelligence (AGI) - a hypothetical AI, also referred to as strong AI or general AI, capable of performing any human task, with broad intelligence across various domains.

artificial intelligence - the science and engineering of making intelligent machines, especially intelligent computer programs.

artificial narrow intelligence (ANI) - also known as weak AI or narrow AI, an AI that's designed to perform specific or limited tasks that typically require human intelligence. Contrast with artificial general intelligence (AGI) which is capable of much broader cognitive abilities.

artificial neural network (ANN) - computational models loosely inspired by the human brain and consisting of layers of artificial neurons arranged in a network that can be trained to learn complex relationships in data, often referred to simply as a neural network.

artificial neuron - a computational model inspired by the neurons in the human brain, designed to process inputs, apply a weighted sum, and produce an output through an activation function, enabling it to participate in learning within neural networks.

backpropagation - a method for adjusting the weights of neurons in hidden layers of a neural network that involves calculating the error of output neurons, then propagating these errors backward through the network, assigning blame to each weight, allowing for adjustment to reduce the loss function and improve prediction accuracy.

bias term - an additional parameter added to a neuron's weighted sum of inputs before applying the activation function. This term is included to give the neuron model more flexibility in fitting the data.

clustering - an unsupervised machine learning algorithm that finds groups, or "clusters," in unlabeled data such that the members within each cluster are as similar as possible, while being as different as possible from members of the other clusters.

compute - in the context of AI, this is often used as a noun, referring to the amount or existence of computational power, likely an evolution of the verb "to compute."

computer vision - a field of AI that enables machines to interpret and make decisions based on visual data, mimicking human visual processing.

convolutional neural network (CNN) - a type of deep neural network, also called a ConvNet, that is primarily used to identify and classify objects in images by applying a series of filters, or kernels, that scan across the image, creating feature maps of increasing abstraction (such as from simple edges to basic shapes to objects) that allow it to handle complex visual tasks such as face recognition.

cost function - the average error of a machine learning model across its entire training set, aggregating the individual loss functions from each training example to evaluate the model's overall performance.

Deep Blue - IBM's chess-playing program that defeated world champion Garry Kasparov in a rematch in New York City in 1997 by a score of 3½–2½.

deep learning - a subset of machine learning involving deep neural networks (DNNs), which have significantly advanced AI capabilities. It's characterized by layers of artificial neural networks that learn from large data sets, making it a crucial component in modern computing.

deep neural network - a neural network with multiple hidden layers between the input and output layers, enabling it to learn complex patterns in data so that it can perform tasks that typically require human intelligence, distinguishing it from shallow neural networks that only have one single hidden layer.

deepfake - a digitally modified or AI-generated image, audio, or video that falsely depicts a real person or situation, often used to mislead, damage reputations, or influence public opinion.

epoch - in machine learning, one complete pass of the algorithm through the entire training data set.

existential threat - in the context of AI, a controversial concern involving the hypothetical scenario in which AI's intelligence increases at an exponential rate until it dwarfs the intelligence of human beings, at which point it poses a risk to the survival of the human species.

expert systems - A group of "classic AI" decision-support systems popular during the 1980s that use predefined rules and knowledge bases in a specific field in order to mimic the decisions that human experts in that field would make, also typically featuring an interface that lets users input information in order to receive direction from the program about how to handle a particular case or situation.

face detection - a type of facial recognition that attempts to determine if a person's face is present in an image or video, and if so, where the face is located.

face identification - a type of facial recognition concerned with determining which face a given face matches in a potentially large database of known faces.

face verification - a type of facial recognition with a goal to determine if a given face matches a specific, known face – the type of program used by your smartphone to unlock your screen.

facial attribute analysis - a type of facial recognition application that is designed to determine traits of the detected face, such as age, gender, and emotional state.

facial recognition - also called face recognition, a family of AI technologies that allows computers to perform tasks such as detecting faces in images and videos (face detection), determining traits of a detected face (facial attribute analysis), determining if a detected face matches a specific, known face (face verification), and matching a detected face with a face in a database of known faces.

features - in the context of machine learning, features are the distinct attributes of each data point, for example the pixels in an image or the words in a text document, that a machine learning algorithm uses to learn from the data and make predictions based on new data that it didn't see in the training process.

feedforward neural network - a type of neural network in which all connections between nodes and layers move information in the same direction within the network, from the inputs toward the outputs, with no loopbacks or cycles within the network.

finetuning - in the context of AI, the second stage of the training process of a large language model in which a base model is modified to create more desirable outputs based on feedback provided by human evaluators.

general purpose AI (GPAI) - defined in an amendment to the EU's AI Act to be *an "AI model, including when trained with a large amount of data using self-supervision at scale, that displays significant generality and is capable* *to competently perform a wide range of distinct tasks regardless of the way the model is placed on the market and that can be integrated into a variety of downstream systems or applications."*

generative adversarial network (GAN) - an AI architecture consisting of a pair of neural networks – a generator that produces "fakes," or outputs that mimic real data such as images or audio, and a discriminator that attempts to distinguish real data from fakes. These two networks train together, enhancing each other's accuracy through a competitive process.

generative AI - AI technologies that can generate content, like text, images, or videos, from user prompts, such as ChatGPT, DALL•E, and Stable Diffusion, raising questions about algorithmic biases and intellectual property rights.

generative pre-trained transformer (GPT) - The name of OpenAI's family of large language models (LLMs), including GPT-3.5 and GPT-4, that leverage the transformer architecture and are exposed to user prompts via the ChatGPT AI chatbot platform and through other applications via an API.

gradient descent - a mathematical technique used in backpropagation to adjust neural network weights that identifies the optimal changes to make each weight in order to minimize the mode's error by seeking a local minimum in the loss function. This iterative process adjusts weights based on the learning rate, aiming to reduce error as efficiently as possible.

graphical processing units (GPUs) - a special type of computer chip originally designed to perform the rapid mathematical calculations required to render rich 3D graphics in fast-paced modern video games, they have been more recently used in parallel to train machine learning models.

hallucination - outputs of large language models that are factually incorrect, nonsensical, and out of touch with reality; confabulations.

hidden layer - any layer in a neural network that is situated in between the input layer and the output layer.

hyperparameter - an aspect of a neural network that the humans creating it determine before the training process begins, and which stays constant throughout the training process. Some examples include the number of hidden layers, the number of neurons per layer, and the choice of activation function of the neurons.

K-means clustering - a specific kind of clustering algorithm in machine learning that iteratively adjusts the partitioning of unlabeled data into a specific number of clusters that the user can define upfront, represented by the letter K.

labeled data - in the context of machine learning, data values that are paired with known, correct outputs, used in supervised learning to train a model to convert inputs into correct outputs.

large language model (LLM) - a deep neural network that commonly uses the transformer architecture and its self-attention mechanisms that enable simultaneous consideration of all tokens in a sequence in order to carry out complex natural language tasks.

loss function - a method of measuring the error of a machine learning model for a single training example, quantifying the difference between the model's predicted output and the actual target output.

machine learning (ML) - an umbrella term describing the branch of AI that involves the study and use of different types of statistical algorithms that are applied to data sets in order to learn from the patterns in those data sets how to accomplish specific tasks.

machine translation - an AI technology that seeks to automatically translate from one language to another without the intervention of a human translator, used in applications like Google Translate.

model - the AI that results from the training process; a trained algorithm.

natural language processing (NLP) - an AI technology that leverages machine learning to process and generate human language, enabling systems to interact with humans via text or voice exchanges.

optical character recognition (OCR) - an AI application that can convert images of printed or hand-written text, such as photographs of checks or automobile license plates, into machine-encoded text.

overfitting - the problem that arises when a model has learned that the noise and irrelevant details present in the training data are important factors to consider when carrying out the task at hand, resulting in poor model performance when presented with unseen data.

parameter - one of many elements of an AI model that the machine learning algorithm adjusts during training to minimize the difference between its output and the correct output, improving its accuracy over time.

perceptron - the first artificial neuron, developed in 1957 by Frank Rosenblatt, that could be trained on data to perform simple binary tasks by multiplying inputs by weights, summing up the products, and then comparing the weighted sum to a threshold, outputting one value (e.g. 1) if the sum is greater than the threshold, and a second value (e.g. -1) if the sum is less than the threshold.

personally identifiable information (PII) - data that could expose an individual's identity, such as Social Security numbers, passport numbers, personal addresses, or telephone numbers.

pretraining - in the context of AI, the first stage of the training process of a large language model in which a base model is created using a massive corpus of text in order to learn general patterns in human language before being fine-tuned on specific tasks.

recommendation system - also known as a recommender, an AI application that provides suggestions for users, such as movies or products, based on their preferences and history.

reinforcement learning - one of the main machine learning approaches in which an AI agent learns to make decisions through rewards and penalties from actions taken, improving outcomes over time.

reinforcement learning through human feedback (RLHF) - a training method where human evaluators assess and score the outputs of large language models like OpenAI's GPT-4, using these assessments to adjust and improve the model's performance, effectively training it to align with human preferences.

self-attention mechanism - an advancement that enables a transformer in a large language model to consider every single token (word, fragment, or letter) in an entire sequence of text at the same time, and thereby to discover complex patterns and relationships between tokens in the entire input.

self-supervised learning - a machine learning approach in which the labels of the training data are created by the system itself instead of being provided by a human teacher or supervisor, for example by constructing its own pairs of inputs and outputs from a large corpus of text.

semi-supervised learning - a combination of supervised learning and unsupervised learning in which models are trained using a small amount of labeled data, and also using a huge amount of unlabeled data.

speech recognition - an AI application that can convert voice inputs into text, enabling virtual assistants to process and respond to human language.

strong AI - a hypothetical AI, also referred to as artificial general intelligence (AGI) or general AI, capable of performing any human task, with broad intelligence across various domains, unlike weak AI which is designed to solve specific or limited problems. The original meaning intended by philosopher John Searle was an AI that can actually understand – a computer with a real mind.

subsymbolic AI - one of the two main branches of AI, it focuses on learning and finding patterns from large amounts of data and places a heavy emphasis on artificial neural networks, with their myriad connected nodes, which has led some to refer to it as "connectionist AI."

superintelligence - a hypothetical AI that possesses an intelligence significantly greater than that of human beings in every aspect.

supervised learning - one of the main machine learning approaches that involves the training of models using labeled data, or input samples paired with their known, correct outputs.

symbolic AI - one of the two main branches of AI, it involves explicit programming of knowledge using predefined rules that make use of human-readable symbols, often referred to as "classic AI" due to its prominence in the early years of the history of the field of AI.

technological singularity - a hypothetical future point, spoken of by technologists like Ray Kurzweil, at which AI enters a continuous and uncontrollable loop of self-improvement that results in an explosion of intelligence that dwarfs the intelligence of human beings.

threshold activation function - the earliest type of activation function that converts the weighted sum of the inputs of a neuron into one of two binary outputs (e.g. 1 or -1) based on whether the weighted sum meets a certain threshold value.

token - a chunk of text – a word, a fragment of a word, a single letter, or even a phrase – that a transformer in a large language model processes using a self-attention mechanism that allows the model to simultaneously consider every single token so that it can find patterns in the entire sequence and generate relevant human language outputs.

transformer - a type of neural network architecture, trained on a vast corpus of text from books and websites, that utilizes a self-attention mechanism to process entire sequences of tokens simultaneously in order to generate humanlike text responses based on prompts submitted by users.

Turing test - another term for Alan Turing's "imitation game," this is a famous test that evaluates an AI's ability to exhibit human-like intelligence, which it would pass successfully if, after five minutes of text-based interaction, a human judge cannot reliably distinguish it from a human.

unlabeled data - in the context of unsupervised learning, real-world datasets whose inputs aren't tagged, or labeled, with corresponding "correct" outputs. Used by models to learn patterns or structures in the data without being explicitly guided by a "supervisor" toward correct outputs.

unsupervised learning - one of the main machine learning approaches that utilizes one of a variety of statistical algorithms, such as clustering, that enable a model to learn from underlying patterns it finds in unlabeled data, or data with inputs that don't have known, correct outputs.

weak AI - also known as artificial narrow intelligence (ANI) or narrow AI, an AI that's designed to perform specific or limited tasks that typically require human intelligence. Contrast with strong AI which is capable of much broader cognitive abilities.

weights - an artificial neuron's parameters, analogous to synaptic strengths between biological neurons in the human brain, that are adjusted during training to improve the neural network's output accuracy.

Made in the USA
Coppell, TX
07 June 2024